Alan Sandall was born and educated in Reading. A jo
editor for 26 years, first in Reading, as the final editor (
1965, then Uxbridge, Bedford and Bath. At 14 he joine
Earlier, when Dunkirk happened, he was in the LDV the night the appeal was made.
Volunteers were sought at his Boy Scout meeting and he went straight on duty, then
home late to tell his Mum. At 13, he joined before his Dad. Looking for something
more rewarding, he found it in the AFS – and, at a true 17, he was the first, and only,
senior messenger of Fire Force 15, covering Berks, Bucks and Oxon. He then joined
the Royal Navy.

Previous book, GOING, GOING, GONE!

To Rob.

Best wishes

Alan J Sandall

10. 2. 93.

***Cover photograph*: Devastation in
Reading's town centre after daylight
hit-and-run raid in which 43 died. Cyril
May took this picture for the Reading
Standard almost immediately.**

FACT is stranger than fiction. This book is based on fact, some from personal experiences. To add authority, senior officers, the fire stations, and firms named are correct, so too, as a tribute, are the men who died. The chief characters of this book, and the stations at which events are described, are an amalgam of many incidents which really happened, all brought together, and are not necessarily in the manner or sequence in which they are here described. Because the events are real some may try to identify individuals. They will waste their time. I trust the firemen and women portrayed in the book will identify with all who served.

I have received great help, and encouragement from many people, particularly veterans of the Royal Berkshire Fire and Rescue Service Old Comrades Association, especially Eddie Lovegrove. My thanks to them all.

Alan Sandall

Are you 17?

by

Alan G Sandall

Alan Sandall of Frome

Dedicated
to the memory of Jeff Robson

A firefighter's fireman – always
fighting for his firemen

First published by Alan Sandall of Frome, Somerset, England, BA11 5JN

February, 1993

© Alan G Sandall, 1993

ISBN 0 9517757 1 5

Typeset and printed by BP Integraphics, Bath

Are you 17?

FIFTY YEARS AGO a holocaust of fire descended on Britain. With the first blitz, in September, 1940, people surged from the country's capital. They were convinced London was going to burn to ashes. Within months words like Coventrate became accepted overnight – and numbingly understood.

Facing the understandably panic-stricken masses escaping along the Great West Road, and undoubtedly every other exit, were the 'Dad's Army' of fire fighters, arriving on their miscellany of scrap-yard transport, and heading for London's Docks.

Their vehicles – towing the vital, new, mass-produced pumps, part of the hurried war preparations – would have been ready-made for the, then unconsidered, future world of television parody. But, the men were not. These were the men, and women, who, seeing the newspapers' accounts of Spain's civil war, volunteered to join the emergent Auxiliary Fire Service – AFS as it became affectionately known.

BUT, it was not all affection. During the silent opening months of World War Two, while others' husbands and boy friends were away with the Armed Services, these men were abused, accused of dodging the war!

They were given white feathers! People thought they were escaping the danger. From the night the bombers showered their high explosives and incendiaries, on a bowed but undefeated Britain, they became heroes. Fighting in the searing heat of a previously unknown hell, they battled until they literally dropped with exhaustion, at times facing starvation – always facing death.

They were the front-line troops who beat the fires which Hitler was certain would bring Britain to surrender.

The fire engine bought by Reading Fire Brigade in 1938. Photographed in its restored livery in 1963 – without white paint and black-out headlamp masks! It is lovingly cared for by the Royal Berkshire Veteran Fire Engine Society. It is loaned to them by Sir N Williamson, himself a former fireman at Mortimer. Photo, Bracknell News.

Foreword

Many books have been written about the Fire Service during the Second World War. What is so unique about 'Are You 17?' is the impressive amount of detailed recall of events displayed by the author. Concentrating, as it does, on Reading in particular, and to some extent Berkshire in general, each chapter provides a fascinating and easily readable picture of what life was really like for the ordinary men and women who struggled to support the defence of their country close to home. It is a timely reminder of just how much we still owe those people, who gave so much.

Garth Scotford
Chief Fire Officer for Royal Berkshire

Author's preface

It takes all types to make a world, as it did to make the fire fighters of World War Two. Few today know it was the bakers and bricklayers, builders and bankers, hairdressers, publicans, shopkeepers ... The list is endless, including the out-of-work and, at least one shrewd, happy tramp.

These were the ordinary, ill-equipped, civilians, from the towns and villages across Britain, who went to war as the largely self-trained AFS. Overnight, in a frightening overture, the volunteers, part-timers as well, learnt a new meaning to fire fighting – and gained a new stature.

It was a war fought without radio communications, when even telephones were rare. Few of the masses could drive.

When the awful war was over and one young hairdresser, who had been in the thick of it, returned to his dad's business, he was cutting the hair of a doctor, a former Royal Naval surgeon. 'Were you in the Services?' asked the doctor. 'Yes' – 'What the Army?' 'No, the Fire Service,' said the hairdresser. 'Oh, I thought you said the Services,' cryptically replied the doctor.

'I bloody well told him,' said the hairdresser.

But it wasn't only those who were themselves away who didn't understand what the firemen faced and suffered. A lady in the same salon after the war, said 'Wasn't it dreadful the way the Germans kept us awake flying over here to Coventry?'

'I don't know, I was in Coventry,' replied the hairdresser.

For those of that era who are left and didn't understand, but especially so that today's generation shall understand, and not forget, this book is written.

Remember: During World War Two more than 1,000 fire fighters, lost their lives, including 25 firewomen, from virtually every county in the country. An eight-foot tall bronze sculpture, depicting three blitz fighters, remembers them. It stands in London, close by St Paul's Cathedral, and was unveiled by the Queen Mother. Her Majesty toured blitzed towns with her husband, King George VI – she saw and knows.

Prime Minister Winston Churchill called them, 'The heroes with grimy faces'. This is my tribute.

AGS

Contents

1 · Decision Day

Harold stopped his cycle against the kerb. He leant back on the left pedal, balanced himself expertly on the deep, main road kerb, folded his arms, and looked around. As a teenager, and with bicycles the normal way of getting about in the desperate years of World War Two, he knew how to handle and get fun out of riding his black, three-speed Raleigh.

Now was the moment of decision. He looked at the dull, grey, building. Had it been a factory? A warehouse? A garage? There was no way of knowing from outside.

At one end of the long plain wall facing the main road was a wooden sliding door, big enough for a lorry to go through. At the other end was a small shop window, nothing in it, and bricked up inside to stop blast. Beside it a small door.

Harold was a Boy Scout and he had been taught the importance of good observation in such troubled times. For a long time his troop had been without a Scoutmaster because everyone had gone to the war and, as one of the patrol leaders, he had read and re-read Baden-Powell's Scouting for Boys. He remembered the stories the Chief Scout told about the importance of understanding from seeing what was going on.

To 'Be prepared', and 'to do his duty', as the promise said, seemed vital to all Scouts as Britain battled alone against the vicious Nazi war machine.

Dare he go in and try to bluff his way into the Auxiliary Fire Service? He was nearly 15, and he was already well used to the war and there was no fear of what joining would mean – it was, well simply, had he got enough cheek!

There was a quiet swish behind him and, quickly looking up, a trolleybus pulled up at its stop. How lucky Reading was to have introduced a fleet of the modern double-deckers, erected the electric supply poles, and put them into service in the months just before the war started in 1939. Without them where would the war-workers be, striving for transport with petrol so scarce.

Smart chocolate in colour, although the broad cream band had been painted down to a narrow line so that the buses, hopefully didn't attract so much attention from the air. As it drew away with hardly a sound Harold smiled ruefully. Coming the opposite way along the main Oxford Road was one of the oldest charabancs he could remember, with big cast radiator, and, on top, a huge rubber bag bulging up and down, appearing to breathe!

The Thames Valley Traction Company's veteran chugged level with Harold and then he could see tacked on the back a trailer, with its own coke fire, creating the methane gas which was stored in the bag to drive the converted engine. It was

1

heading for Didcot – and the 'ssshh' Government ordnance depot, although the destination board would not say so – and likely to make it. Well it did regularly every day.

There was a war on – definitely if people could improvise like that, and were prepared to travel like that.

That was it, Harold's mind was made up. He stepped off his cycle and straight up to the door, knocked and walked in. Inside was a bare counter and nobody. No time for quitting, Harold took a deep breath and banged hard on the counter – 'What else are empty counters for?' went through his young mind.

'Yes' said the smartly dressed officer who appeared. Harold knew he was an officer by the buttons down the single-breasted coat, and the patch pockets. Firemen wore double-breasted tunics. The voice was clipped, authorative, and very nearly intimidating from such a short man. Yet he looked kindly, as though his was a much-changed world.

Harold took another deep breath, trying not to show it. 'I want to join the AFS as a messenger,' he said. The officer looked him up and down, as best he could from the other side of the counter. It clearly wasn't the first such request he had received – by early 1941, firemen knew all about needing volunteers to help.

At the same time, he wasn't sure; this boy did look young, or did he? He was tall, fair haired, and he handled himself confidently. 'I am Patrol Officer Harry Spatcher and I am second in charge,' he said, making up his mind. 'You will have to see Station Officer Sharp and he is out.' If the boy was really keen, he would come back; if not the problem would solve itself.

Harold's keen eyes had caught sight of the 'fire engines' in the background even as the officer spoke. He looked again: there was a 1936 Morris 10 car looking so tiny with a long ladder strapped on top, with rolls of hose between the rungs, and a trailer pump hitched on behind; another car, and a smart-looking Austin open lorry, again laden with ladders and hoses, with a larger trailer pump.

In that second, all was clear. 'What time will he be here?' The answer was 5 pm. With a smart, thank you, Harold was gone.

*   *   *

Cycling home Harold made up his mind, it was troop night so he would wear his uniform back to the fire station. Scout uniforms were well respected, boys undertook all kinds of war emergency service.

He looked smart when he cycled back to the emergency fire station. Badges on his arm, his patrol leader's emblem shining on the front of his broad brimmed hat. The main road was much busier when he parked back on the kerb. He was early, of course, so he sat back and watched. The trolley-buses were going to The Three Tuns and the Bear Inn, nothing useful for invaders.

The last shoppers were going in and out of the Co-op opposite. They didn't seem to have much in their bags, and the glued paper strips criss-crossing the plate glass windows, to stop flying splinters if there was bomb blast, were looking tired – like the people.

A tiny Tiger Moth biplane flew sedately over, fairly high up, heading back to Woodley Aerodrome, or would it be White Waltham? Both aerodromes were frantically training new pilots. Nobody took special notice, it was part of the wartime scene.

Suddenly, there was a snarling roar as a modern fighter plane ripped over flying very low. Every head shot up. There was no time to run for shelter, or need. Harold had been looking that way, following the trainer plane, and he realised it was a Spitfire, not a raiding Messerschmitt. It was easy to pick out with its curved wing tips. The pilot was following the river, heading home to Benson, near Wallingford, another of those places not to be talked about. But, go hiking with the Scouts and you were bound to know! But not tell.

The moment of truth, well figuratively speaking. Harold straightened his hat – everybody knew the Scout hat – fingered his neckerchief and white leader's lanyard, and headed for the door. This time Station Officer Sharp was there. 'You want to join the fire service?' It was definitely a question. And one that meant you do the talking!

'Yes please,' said Harold, then realising that sounded polite but not very mature, he added, 'I do.' 'You are 17 and you want to be a messenger?' came the next question, as the officer eyed Harold up and down.

Harold reached for his sleeve and pointed to his fireman's badge. 'I did my training at the town centre fire station and passed first time. I can couple a hydrant, run out hose, put up a ladder (he didn't add that he had to drive himself awful hard to climb it to a real height), and I know my knots. And I have my ambulance badge.' That was one of the really tough badge tests and, uniquely, the badge, with its red cross, had a special place at the top of both arms.

Although he wasn't saying, clearly the officer had quite a knowledge of Scouts: it was instinct, they had done so much to help the firemen in the dreadful days of the past winter, well mainly the nights of those dreadful months.

'You also have your pioneering and camping badges, so you know a lot more than just a fireman's knots – and about surviving!' 'Yes, and I am working for my First Class, and, hopefully, to become a King's Scout,' replied Harold

It seemed the officer's mind was made up. 'You say you are 17, what is your birthday?' That was clever, thought Harold. 'January 23,' he replied, carefully avoiding the year that he had not been asked to tell. The officer wrote it down together with his name, Harold Randle.

'You will have to go to the main Caversham Road fire station to collect your equipment and to be measured for your uniform. Then I want you to come back and meet our longest-serving messenger, Len Hall. He will tell you the routine. He's on duty tomorrow night.'

There was a pause, as Station Officer Harold Sharp reflected. 'It's tough, it's going to be tough, but I think you will enjoy it. Best of luck.'

Putting out his hand to the Scout, the two Harolds shook hands warmly. Just how 'warm' life was going to become wasn't something the young Harold could imagine. There wasn't even anything like a King's shilling to show he had joined. And you had to use your own bike at all times.

3

At the Caversham Road fire station Harold was lucky, he was recognised by Henry Barnes, one of the firemen who had given instruction for the badge. 'I've just joined the AFS as a messenger at the Oxford Road station. Mr Sharp has sent me down to collect my equipment and be measured for my uniform.'

'Good show. You've found the right man,' he replied. 'Come with me.'

Henry was quite expert and swift at measuring. 'You will like the uniform, it's tailor-made to fit and the quality is good, too. It will take about a week.'

Then from the racks he pulled a steel helmet, with the AFS insignia, not right the first time, it needed a bigger size! Then a service respirator, just like soldiers wore. Harold helped as Henry hung the case round his neck, strapping it tight on his chest. Then Henry pulled out the headpiece, with its big eyes and umbilical tube. Harold tucked his head in, chin first, as he was told, and got used to the strange claustrophobic feeling as Henry pulled the straps tight.

'Can you breathe?' Harold nodded. Henry got hold of it just below the neck and yanked it out and upwards, so that it came off with the straps still in the correct position, ready for use! 'Take care of it. Sling the helmet round the case and you will always have both with you.' He added, 'You will be getting plenty of drill with the gasmask on!'

Next a pair of wellington boots, well rubbed down the side where they had been used before by a despatch rider. 'You can't have everything new, there's a war on,' he grunted, seeing Harold's look. 'Here's a new set of cyclist's waterproof coat and leggings, they will be really useful.'

With his arms loaded up, there was one more special piece of equipment. Almost with ceremony, Henry produced an old-style cycle oil lamp with the word FIRE painted across the 2½ inch diameter glass. 'Put that on a bracket on your front fork,' he said with all sincerity. There was a wick and oil in the tiny tank, and that was the hardest of all the gear to juggle home on his bicycle. As he rode, he suddenly realised that it was not costing a single clothing coupon – just as well, he had none left.

*　　*　　*

The sirens wailed their alarm during the night. Harold woke and stretched in his bed. He wondered about the future. All was quiet as he pondered: mum and dad were asleep, at least he guessed dad would be, tired out with long days at work and the rest of the time taken up with the Home Guard motor transport section.

He slipped out of bed and from the window watched the searchlights weaving their patterns. But there was no deadly throb of the German planes with the creeping horror feeling which came with the noise of their engines, apparently out of synchronisation.

The one-note whine of the All Clear came quickly and he went back to bed without any clear idea of what was to come, at least it was going to be more fun than the Home Guard where, he remembered again, he could strip a Lewis machine gun faster than most men, but they wouldn't let him fire it!

Early evening found him back at the fire station, his gasmask and helmet over his shoulder and his waterproofs strapped behind his saddle. Len Hall was waiting to greet him. The big garage door was open; there was room for a big vehicle, behind was a large trailer pump and, at the side, ladders, hose, ropes, shovels, and a host of other gear.

'Welcome, bring your bike in,' he said warmly. 'Don't park it near that lot, we're waiting for the night lorry.' That was a puzzle but Harold said nothing. 'Come and have a look around.'

Len was clearly a lot older and knew the ropes. 'This used to be a garage for laundry vehicles. You will still find some bags of soap powder at the back, but it's good to stop blast! He explained, the office by the counter was now the control room, it sounded grand but he explained it had a telephone and the man on duty kept the log book and took messages. 'You book on and off duty there.'

Len climbed a metal ladder to a platform room above lorry height, there was a tortoise stove glowing in the middle. It was formerly the mechanics rest room. 'This is where we make tea, and people eat whatever they bring with them.' Looking up Harold saw the glass windows in the roof were all painted black, no light was going to creep through them. It was very different from the all-mod-cons of the purpose-built Caversham Road station which the Corporation built and was opened just in time, two months after the war started in September 1939.

'Come and see the bunk room, when there's time to sleep,' added Len drily. Passing back beside the counter they slipped through a side door and up some narrow stairs. At the top, in a room the width of the shop and passage below, were double-tier bunks with a hard mattress, pillow and a blanket.

Harold did not want to appear a moaner so he made his 'It's pretty basic' sound casual. 'The firemen made them themselves, nothing was provided,' said Len. He casually lifted the corner of one of the palliases and Harold could see the chicken wire base.

'Come on, let's find a quiet corner and I will tell you what happens.' Len explained that some of the firemen were full-time, although most had joined as part-time volunteers at the beginning, before the war started. They worked 9 am until 7 pm, and then the other shift took over, with a 'short day' to change over. If the sirens sounded then they had to come back just like the part-time firemen and messengers.

'As a messenger you will be on duty at least one night a week and on call when the siren goes.' Len laughed; 'So you could be here most nights of the week, if things go on as they have recently!'

There was a noise at the garage door and a scruffy Bedford builder's lorry started backing in. The firemen appeared and, as it stopped, hitched up the sturdy looking trailer pump. It was obviously a well rehearsed routine – boring and tedious – learnt as a necessity.

'Come and give a hand,' said Len, adding, casually, 'You had better find out as

5

much as you can as quickly as possible, I am off to join the Royal Navy in a fortnight.'

The ladder was already hitched into place and Harold bent to pick up a roll of the new American rubber-lined canvas hose. Phew, it was dammed heavy, much more than the flax hose he used at Caversham Road. Then he was steered to one of the big coils of rope. He struggled with it, until with a friendly laugh one of the firemen – very tall and strong – took it and heaved it over the sideboard on to the lorry.

The builder's driver had already shouted 'Good night' and gone. The thought that strangers were going to take over his lorry, and hammer it, was by now a daily matter of fact and nothing he could worry about. The tall fireman picked up a notebook and wrote down the mileage and checked the petrol. They were ready with an extra fire engine!

Other lorries would appear when the sirens sounded. Firm's drivers had to turn out, just like firemen. Then there would be frantic activity loading all the gear aboard to go to the dispersal action points – and off when they came back! explained Len.

'If you ride that builder's lorry watch out,' said Len. 'You have to throw your cycle aboard and climb up and hang on amongst the gear. But, watch the floor! There are some bloody big holes in the planking and it could be very painful.'

The realisation that the Auxiliary Fire Service was really struggling to make do, came home. It reminded him of the chaos the night the LDV, the Local Defence Volunteers, was started and he, as a 13-year-old Scout, joined. He shook the thought from his mind, Len was speaking again.

'The important thing is that messengers are vital to get messages through if the telephone lines are down. But, first and foremost in the AFS you will learn to be a fireman. Men can be knocked out just as easy as telephones.

'We have had quite a year,' said Len. 'Everybody was on absolute edge last May but nothing really seemed to happen. Drilling and practice turnouts, and ruddy yellow warnings.' He sighed, 'They kept us on our toes, we were all being called in every time it was possible. Firemen were even coming to fetch me,' Len explained, perhaps with an emphasis on how everyone was important.

'Then – on Friday, May 10th, I shall remember that day – the Chief Officer ordered that all leave was cancelled until further notice. Full uniform was to be worn all the time and nobody was to leave town without special permission from himself. And, gasmasks and steel helmets were to be carried!'

'That stirred things up,' said Len. 'An hour later there was a telephone call saying 'All men on holidays must be recalled'.' He laughed and said, 'We all wondered what was going to happen.' What happened was a lot more drill, especially with gasmasks, and practice alerts.

Everyone was expected to report on duty as soon as a yellow warning was received, he explained. 'We were all dashing round calling out the off-duty full-timers. That couldn't last, it was too exhausting and the order came they were not to be called until the red, that's the siren,' he said with relief.

Stirrup pumps were in big demand and men from the stations were busy handing them out and showing volunteer street parties how to use them. 'Including afternoon demonstrations to housewives. They were all involved.

'I remember 300 people at a demo in Windsor Drive one evening, and later at 11.18 pm the siren was sounding.' Harold listened intently as Len explained the routine at such times. Cars and lorries permanently on duty went off to action stations, plus Warwicks' lorry which came in every evening. Then Lewis's lorry would arrive, followed by Collins, and so on.

Within seven minutes 26 men were at the station to reinforce the night staff, followed quickly by a further 14, plus six messengers. 'Nine units go out from this tiny station.' Proudly he said, 'Our woman telephonist was there within two minutes.' 'Then there weren't many women in the AFS.' He noted, 'That alarm lasted until half past three in the morning!' adding ruefully, 'That was before they were sounding all night.'

Len explained that there was a sub-station in a lean-to garage behind the Prince of Wales pub, in Tilehurst, with reinforcements dashing there as well. Two crews and pumps operated from there.

'We also had to be the telephone contact for the LDV, when they started. They were operating with their headquarters at Barclays Bank, along the road.

'It was strange one night, the LDV – Home Guard now, of course – were alerted on the yellow but their stand-down didn't come until four hours after ours! Everybody was frightened about parachutists. Another night they were on alert for three Germans who had escaped capture. They baled out when their bomber was crashing. It came down near East Woodhay, Kingsclere.

'We had two men on guard duty at the station, day and night for months.' He ended, 'That is enough for tonight.

'Be here early Sunday morning for drill with the other part-timers. By then work out all the back streets to get through to Caversham Road station, that's the headquarters and the main routes could be blocked.

'Oh, you wouldn't know, it's kept quiet, but the regional headquarters to control all civil defence, is operating from Marlborough House in Parkside Road, off Tilehurst Road. Make sure you know which it is, you never know!' He added, conversationally, 'A lot of the clerical staff are from Huntley and Palmers biscuit factory, so you might well know somebody if you go there.'

Clearly that was enough for one visit. 'Wish me a quiet night,' said Len, 'everybody can do with one. See you on Sunday.'

*   *   *

Sunday was a nice dry, bright morning. Thank goodness, thought Harold. He put on well-worn old clothes – he couldn't run risks of damaging his suit with clothing coupons so precious. He collected up his thick gaberdine cyclist's waterproofs. Then, proudly, he put his gasmask and steel helmet over his shoulder and left home for the fire station. His quaint 'Fire' oil lamp was clamped to the front fork!

There were quite a number of firemen and messengers gathering as he got there. He followed into the control room and announced, 'Messenger Randle on duty.'

Most were strangers – all were friendly. A couple he recognised. There was a man called Victor by the others, whom he knew lived a few streets away from home and was involved in whatever the secret work was at the Brooke Bond factory. It used to print labels for the tea packets. Another ran a nursery gardens in Tilehurst, but he couldn't think of his name.

Out into the appliance room, as the garage was grandly called, came Station Officer Sharp. 'Patrol Officer Spatcher will take the part-timers into Richmond Road for drill,' he announced. 'Take a Worthington Simpson light pump, you can manhandle it easily. I want you to keep changing over to each others' jobs, so that you can cope in a emergency.

'Full-timers will stay here, check the equipment and then get some rest. We could soon be on blitz relief again,' he added slowly.

Quickly unhitching the light pump from the Morris car, the men squeezed it through the small gap in front of the sorry-looking hard-used builder's lorry and across the main road.

Harold with his Scout training for his fireman's badge was soon able to make himself valuable and win a place in a crew as they took their turns. First time, he had to grab the standpipe and key, run from the pump to the water main cover in the road, hook it off, and drop in the standpipe. As he locked on the lugs and yanked it tight, another fireman snapped on the hose and went running away to connect it to the pump. Into the hole went Harold's key, seeking the square ended 'tap', ready for the order 'Water on'.

The pump man had started its engine; far along the road two other firemen were almost ready connecting the nozzles to the hoses which they had run out. Just as the fireman in charge looked ready to shout the 'Water on' instruction to Harold, Patrol Officer Spatcher screamed: 'Gas!'

Harold saw the others knock their steel helmets off their heads, so that they hung from the shoulders held by the chin straps around the neck, and grabbed into their gasmask cases stretched across their chests. With a quick jutting of their chins, the masks were on, straps tight over their heads and steel helmets back on top.

It all happened within seconds, seven he was told later, but Harold wasn't far behind. Next moment the fireman at the pump was waving his arms excitedly – he wanted the water turned on at the hydrant, and no way could his voice be heard, so he signalled.

A quick pull on the key and water gushed from the main and filled the hose as it crept swiftly to the pump. Equally swiftly the pump man used his engine to send it under more pressure to the two at the branches, for Harold remembered his badge test and that was what the nozzles were called.

It seemed ages shut inside the gasmask; hot, too, in his gaberdine waterproofs and wellingtons. Harold could hardly see, he hadn't used enough of the special demister on the inside of the glass eyes of the mask and was badly steamed up.

Dimly he could see the pump man waving his arms across his head, the sign to turn off the water. Harold wound the key clockwise, the hose shrank like a wounded snake. The others were taking off their gasmasks and Harold followed suit. 'Well done, messenger,' said Mr Spatcher. Then to all the men, he said 'Now we will run the whole drill with gasmasks on.'

There was no doubt that everyone in the know still feared that the Nazis would use gas! Harold stood back and waited for his turn to come again – he knew he was going to sweat before the session was out. And it was going to be the first of many, because these men were keen and they weren't going to let the Germans bomb them into surrender.

2 · First night

Harold's adrenalin was running pretty fast as Tuesday night came. He had said Goodnight to his worried mother – Thank goodness, dad's duty was a different night, normally a weekend because of his work.

He took his cycle in through the small door and parked it. Into the control room he walked. 'Messenger Randle reporting for all night duty,' he said. The fireman didn't seem too comfortable sitting at a desk, Harold sensed he preferred to be out risking getting cold and wet.

Station Officer Sharp was also there, Was he always on duty?, thought Harold. 'You will be riding on Gerrish's coal lorry, so you can put your bicycle straight aboard.' He laughed as he saw the look on Harold's face. 'Don't worry, it's perfectly clean. We took it over when it was new, after the war started – and it has hardly been used for carrying sacks of coal.'

Putting his cycle over the sideboards, it was in absolute contrast to the builder's lorry. A smart grey Austin, there was a shine from the chrome on the black bonnet. Hitched on behind was one of the big pumps. He walked round and studied the controls. A small plate said it was a Coventry Climax – that seemed a piece of poetic own-back after the terrible raids, peaking in the blitz which wiped out the city's cathedral and brought that new war verb, to 'Coventrate'.

Harold took in all the controls, he was going to find a book on how to start and operate it. 'I might be the only one left to keep it going,' he mused to himself, just like a youngster would. He couldn't realise how prophetic that thought would become. Nor could he know that a Southend fireman was awarded a George Medal for keeping his pump operating when the rest of the crew were wiped out.

The leading fireman in charge of the crew riding the Austin came over. 'Hello, you're a new face? My name is Roger Smith. Come and join the others. This evening we are going to have a session for recently joined men to become familiar with pumps and how they work.'

Roger was the instructor. 'You will all have seen and ridden on the variety of weird, clapped out, towing vehicles we have been given by the Corporation. Well, don't judge the pumps the same way. Some people, thank God, at Munich time, were desperately preparing for this war.

'The damage caused by the German bombers in Spain at least woke some people, if not the councils.' He sounded somewhat bitter for a minute but went on again. 'These pumps, 23,000 of them, were built in a great rush and issued to fire brigades in towns and villages all across the country.

'These are the machines that have saved the day! They are great little workers –

10

when you have enough water!' Again there was that edge of bitterness, as he mentally turned back the clock to the previous year.

'Towing these pumps to blitzes, in tatty convoys of cars and lorries, volunteers like you have become ace fire fighters overnight. Make sure you learn well.'

Time and again that evening the pump engine was started, the thick suction hoses screwed together and joined to the pump, and then by gesture thrown into an imaginary pond. Without water, they were trying to master how water could be persuaded to rise inside the hose by suction (sucking out the air), into the impeller spun by the engine, and onwards, through the hoses. Keenness kept the men at it, long after the exercise formally ended. Harold joined those who were staying the night as they climbed the metal steps to the tiny mess room. The kettle was boiling on the anthracite stove, which kept it warm as well.

'Cup of tea?' said Roger, the leading fireman. 'Yes, please.' Roger obviously wanted him to feel at home. The others were pulling out an assortment of bags and packets, with an equally assorted collection of snacks. Not much in any of them, of course, because their rations at home were little enough for the whole week.

Opposite was a broad Oxfordshire man, his name it appeared was Sam, he pulled out a huge raw onion with a piece of bread. He knew how to grow them, and how to keep them that late in the season. Others groaned as the smell spread – it clearly wasn't the first. Sam groaned back, 'This pool margarine is terrible. Why didn't they keep Stork.'

Even without the intrusion of the onion, most of the men were keen to go to bed. They wanted to get some sleep before the alerts started. Roger said he would stay up and hold the fort: 'In any case, I reckon we will have a yellow warning in an hour or so, I can feel it in my bones.' Again it was that touch of cynicism, because Roger had no knowledge that he was right by accident. He was beginning to believe, or hope, that 'they' in high places had worked out a way of knowing where the bombers were heading. 'They' had, intercepting German radio waves, but it was a best kept secret.

'A yellow warning?' said Harold. 'Yes, there are three warnings, yellow, purple, and red – that's when the siren sounds. It gives all the Civil Defence services and, of course the ack-ack and searchlight batteries, a better chance to be ready. It also means we lose a lot more sleep!'

There was a short pause, then Roger said, 'The whole war has been absolutely crazy. Town and city councillors across most of the country never wanted to spend any money to be ready – only special Government grants.' He explained that if it wasn't for fellows like those he had just met, risking their lives and suffering terrible hardships, this country might well have been beaten by the bombers. 'Yet, a year ago some were even being given white feathers – some fools thought we were dodging the Army!'

'Do you know how the Auxiliary Fire Service started? How it was scrimped and scraped out of almost nothing?' 'Please,' said Harold, instinctively his future career as a journalist was pumping him up. He wriggled back into the very second-hand chair, and got a bit nearer to the anthracite stove. Roger was feeling the strain of the hell of the months past and the instinctive reporter's coaxing looks and questions, had turned the key to release the pent-up aggravations. 'Let me tell you a story ...'

That's as far as he got. 'Yellow warning,' shouted the fireman from the control room, loudly so that everyone would hear. Everybody started to stir, 'It's purple now,' came another cry. The sirens started their wail, the rise and fall of the note a clear warning to all so deadened with sleep that it was the start and not the finish of an alert.

'Christ, that's quick,' said Roger, jumping to his feet, all thought of his intention to put the world to rights forgotten. 'Come on, we all disperse, so if a bomb hits the station only one crew will get it.'

He was half way down the iron steps, with Harold following. From out of the darkness – there was just the dim glow from the couple of bulbs in the 'appliance room' – at the front of the building, came a grinding, creaking noise as the big door was pushed sidewards, out of the way down the side wall.

The shabby old builders' Bedford started first pull and drove out with firemen hanging on atop the ladders and hose. The smart Austin coal lorry was equally ready, and did a tight turn, so that it could go out through the same door. Slick driving thought Harold. He was hanging on to his bicycle as well as keeping his own grip. He didn't really know what to expect, but he could see he was learning fast!

There was a moon which meant Harold could see what was happening. Both lorries turned right towards the outskirts of town. Already the men around were cursing at the brightness of the night. 'Bloody Jerries can see for miles,' grunted one.

The Bedford turned right into the gateway of what Harold recognised as the big Co-operative bakery; the Austin kept roaring up the hill nobly dragging the heavyweight of its pump behind. 'If Jerry ever hits that bakery, don't be holding a jet pouring water into that main building,' said the grunter. 'There's a 3,300 volt electric cable coming out of the earth in the middle and you'll be electrocuted – fried – as the current comes back up the water to the brass branch!' The 14-year-old shook for a second or two, 'I'll remember that.' It was a good, if frighteningly real, lesson.

His own lorry suddenly slowed and turned left into a dark, silent looking brickworks. The overhead railway which brought the clay from the pit was stopped. It was as if nothing was happening. Perhaps there was no need for top quality hand-made red bricks in wartime?

It turned in the yard and everybody got off. Harold looked at the sky, realising that the rest were doing the same. The fingers of the searchlights were probing, the dreaded strange note of a German bomber could be heard but it was away in the distance.

Nothing happened, and there seemed nowhere warm to go. The firemen walked about and, encumbered by the ever present gasmask cases, slapped their arms across their bodies to keep warm. Clearly they were bored with this routine, although for Harold it was all new and exciting.

'Why come to a dead old brickworks?' asked Harold. 'Dead,' said Roger, 'they store torpedoes in there!' Roger didn't say and, chilled at the thought, Harold didn't ask if they filled them as well. He never did find out.

A few ack-ack guns could be heard in the distance but clearly Jerry was not coming their way. Piercing through the still night, the strident one note of the All Clear said it was all over – or should be. Three or four alerts a night were not uncommon at this stage of the war.

'Half an hour,' said Roger, looking at his watch. 'Come on men, unhitch the pump and let's turn the lorry round and go home!' There was heavy humour on the last word, he meant the fire station, which they saw far more of than their wives.

Within the backcloth of the main drama being suffered by many somewhere else, suddenly came one of their own. The hitch pin was taken out and the lorry, slowly backed up to the re-arranged position of the pump. It was a regular routine. Roger was ready to connect up when the trailer pump refused to move back the vital few feet – it's own mechanical handbrake was snatched on. Roger was pinned between the lorry and the towbar of the pump. He couldn't get out.

In critical seconds, which seemed like minutes to Harold, Roger was being skewered where it would ruin him for life! Desperate shrieks from the rest saved him. The driver stopped, and moved away again. Roger collapsed to the floor, white faced and gasping. The war was forgotten. He was a popular fireman in charge of this crew and there was unanimous relief as he got his breath back and crawled into the cab, sore and sorry.

'Poor bloke, but he's all right,' said the grunter in a much softer, kindlier voice. 'Did you know his best friend, Gordon at the Wokingham Road station, was lucky not to lose his life in the Pompey blitz? That was the night the Newbury men were killed.'

3 · Escape – No escape

Approaching Portsmouth during a raid was like attending a gala performance of a huge outdoor theatre. As the trail of raggle-taggle cars, taxis, and lorries, pulling their trailer pumps, approached the top of the glistening white chalk hills of Portsdown, the audience gave a little cheer.

There was not much laughter left in them for they were the crowds who fled their homes nightly to the comparative safety of the open countryside. Mums, children, and some dads.

As the AFS crews reached the summit they then became the audience. Ahead, above and below, the action. A backcloth of barrage balloons, and searchlights criss-crossing backwards and forwards, from warships as well as the land. Into this swept the attacking planes, bombs flickering into light clusters as they struck home, the harsh clattering of the aircrews' machine gunners at work.

The chorus responded in opposition to the actors, from little Lewis guns to massive turret guns on the ships, with the orchestration of the batteries of 3.5s playing the main tune.

Berkshire's firemen were among the many brave men making up such aid-cum-quickly. Roger Smith was among them. So too was Gordon Castle, with a unit from his station, Hamilton Road garage, on the other side of town.

For Gordon, the strangeness of the night had started earlier! A telephone call had ordered him to go from the station and collect His Majesty's Regional Inspector of Fire Services. He took H M Smith to Marlborough House, the Parkside Road HQ. 'Have a drink,' he was invited, 'We might be out all night.'

While Gordon drank, the regional officer was on the telephone. 'Are you on regional call tonight?' he asked, when he came back. 'Yes.' 'I have an idea you will be going to Portsmouth! There's a raid on there.'

It was not long before the call arrived and Gordon, with his crew, charged off at the fastest pace they could manage with their elderly, upright ex-Vincent's taxi.

A strange sight as they made their way, travelling alone. Only the tiny slits of the official headlamp masks, and no road signs to guide them – the threat of invasion had swept all signs away to confuse German troops. Although Gordon was in charge he was driving, as so often happened because there were few drivers, and he knew the way, 'Before the war my family used to go down to Hayling Island,' he muttered conversationally.

'Report to Fareham fire station,' was the instruction, he told his crew. 'Never tell you much,' 'Don't think they know,' replied the man beside him.

As they neared the coast they met up with others, all on the same mission. As

14

they cleared the top, saw the blitz still going on, and started to run down Stonor Hill, Gordon made another crash-box gear change. The lever snapped off in his hand. 'Here, you can have this,' he said, thrusting the length of metal into his passenger's hands. Despite the handicap, Gordon kept going by slipping the clutch.

When he pulled into Fareham, there was Mr Smith! Gordon was puzzled and thought 'How the devil did he get here so quickly?' But it was the regional controller who looked most surprised. 'You haven't been keeping to 30 mph?'

'No,' said Gordon. Mr Smith laughed, 'Well I left straight away and I have only just arrived.'

He turned to the officer in charge of Fareham and said, 'Just for his sauce send him into Gosport.'

There were high-explosive bombs and incendiaries falling all around, but nothing touched them, as the crew set off. One bomb dropped a hundred yards in front and blew a hole in the road. Gordon edged on to a grass verge to get by, nothing was easy with just the stub of a gear lever.

Walking into the tiny control room of the Gosport station to report, Gordon eyed suspiciously the big wooden post which was keeping the ceiling up. It was not going to fall on him because, immediately, he was told, 'Report to the High Street, to the officer in charge.' Bald as that.

When the crew got there, there was not a soul to be seen, buildings were burning on each side of the road. Clearly these were not the top priority. That was the big boat-builder's yard, Camper and Nicholsons.

'We will have to go down to the slope used by the Portsmouth car ferry. We can pump from there.' For six to seven hours Gordon and his chaps kept pumping water on the inferno. 'We are just holding it back but we need help,' said Gordon.

A Bofors gun was just above them on the slipway. They jumped at first to its 'whoomp, whoomp' but were soon immune to the noise, but all night long had to keep jumping, getting out of the way of the shell cases it was slinging out all around them.

The incendiaries were giving them the willies, as the planes came in dropping even more. There was a weird whistling as they came down. It lit the place like daylight. All dived under the vehicle.

Gordon looked at the chap who faced him from the other side. 'Cor, you should see your face now, it's dead white.' Gordon laughed as he said it, but he knew he was just as scared.

'What are we doing here?' asked Gordon. 'Our backsides are sticking out!'

Fortunately, they were not hit. But a Southampton fireman was badly hurt by the new explosive incendiaries.

Soon Gordon's plea was answered. Some London firemen arrived. They set up a relay of pumps to surround the boatyard blaze, using Gordon's pump to provide the water from the sea.

'Go and get a cup of tea,' said one of the London officers, 'We can hold the fort now.' Thankfully, Gordon and his crew set off. At the town hall tea was being dispensed from a big milk churn. Dipping their cups in to get a drink, they sat down tired but grateful.

15

Bombs were still dropping and there was a loud explosion from the direction whence they came. 'Come on, we had better get back,' stirred Gordon. It was another nightmare walk, when they reached the slipway, the found their pump completely buried by the debris the bomb had thrown up! 'That cuppa saved us,' whispered a shaken Gordon.

Beneath the mound the pump was still working, pumping water to the fire without any leaks. And it kept on running until it ran out of petrol. Meanwhile Gordon and his crew found other work, and kept hard at it.

As the tide went out in the morning light, Gordon could see hundreds of incendiaries stuck in the mud – at least those hadn't gone off.

It was lunchtime when they were released to drive home – to explain why they were without their pump. 'It was a pretty hectic night,' reported Gordon. 'The buzz was that the Jerries dropped about 23,000 incendiaries, and some 33 landmines. I didn't count them, sir!' he added.

The pump was retrieved and a fortnight later returned to Reading.

*   *   *

The Newbury firemen were already on stand-by down at the coast, ready to give immediate assistance wherever the bombers struck. Seven were in the squad, two were part-timers. In charge was Albert Miles. At 41, he had 12 years service with the Newbury Volunteer Fire Brigade, a force with a proud long-standing reputation. The others were members of the AFS. Recently Albert had been put in charge of training the town's full-time AFS.

The seven-strong crew were ordered into Portsmouth, into the thick of the blazing inferno. Dodging bombs and weaving round craters, they kept their place in the small convoy. The leading vehicle stopped and the Newbury men got out to see what was wrong. Suddenly there was a swishing noise.

'Dive to the ground,' shouted Leslie Fray as he heard the bombs coming. There was a terrific blast and splinters were tearing through his clothes. He had been hit in the shoulder and leg but he tried to pick himself up. Dazed, he was hardly able to see amid the smoke and dust.

Some of his mates were groaning. 'Take it easy,' he said as he tried to find them. As he crawled towards the cries, first-aid men came running to help. Together they did what they could. Then, it seemed almost immediately, one of the American ambulances – which had been sent over as a gift – drove up. The firemen were taken to a clearing station where a first aid party dressed their wounds before sending them on to hospital

Fellow AFS fireman Victor Carr was badly hurt in the back but he forced himself to stand up as he heard Leslie call. 'I must help to find our pals,' he said. The news was not good. Charles Rawlings, aged 37, had been killed instantly, the other six were injured. A few hours later, news from the hospital was that two more had died – their leader, Albert Miles, and Leslie Ford, just 28.

Later that Tuesday morning Fireman Fray underwent an operation to remove the splinters from his shoulder, and then persuaded the doctor to let him return to

Newbury. The others, including Leslie Eggleton and Stephen Whiteman, were kept in hospital.

Back home he paid tribute to the nurses and the first aid parties, who were so cheerful and stood up to the strain so courageously. 'Our men, too, in spite of their wounds, showed great heroism,' he said.

Reading's firemen had a special task, to give succour to Vic Carr's sister, Dolly, for she was their cook at the Caversham Road station.

The blanket of Press and radio censorship, to prevent any useful information reaching the Nazis, allowed the Newbury Weekly News to tell the story of the men's bravery but not where it happened. All that could be reported was '... during an air raid on a town in the South of England on Monday night.'

The people of the Berkshire market town were grief stricken – just like other towns before them, and many more yet to come. Silent crowds were lining the streets when the Newbury VFB engine passed by carrying the body of Fireman Albert Miles, followed by two AFS tenders with the other men.

Union Jacks covered the coffins which had laid in state in the parish church. Business everywhere stopped; shops closed, blinds were down. Sadness was tinged with a sense of pride.

More than a thousand people were jammed in and around the church. The Mayor and Corporation, hundreds of uniformed firemen from many brigades, and Civil Defence personnel, filled the centre. Hats for the women of the town's first-aid parties were steel helmets.

The rector said all three 'gave their lives to save others.' The huge crowd was conscious that the three had responded for their country in its hour of need, but also mindful that all were married men of Newbury, Albert with five children, including a baby; Charles with one, and Leslie, two, the youngest nine months.

A detachment of Police led the long procession from the church to the cemetery at Shaw. Floral tributes were many and, if there had been a Fifth Column agent he would have seen flowers for all three from the Portsmouth Fire Services. A touching tribute which blitzed towns and cities were having to send to many others.

It was also a salutary reminder of the danger the men, part-timers among them, faced as they dashed off at a moment's notice and were often gone for days, without their wives knowing where or how they were surviving!

'I shall always remember that funeral,' said Roger, answering Harold's tactful question. 'We sent wreaths and a lot of us went down. It was quite a parade. There were flowers and firemen from many brigades, from neighbouring counties as well as Berkshire.

'In the Newbury paper, next to the pictures of the funeral procession, there was a plea from the Regional Commissioner for more people to come forward as fire watchers, to beat the fire bombs. About time too.'

He grunted, 'He also said we could expect heavy action by the enemy in the next few weeks. He was right about that.'

Less than three hours after Roger, and the rest, were back from the funeral a purple warning was given. Six minutes later the sirens sounded.

4 · War clouds

Rape of Austria by Hitler, and then his march into the Sudetandland; Mussolini's conquest of Abyssinia; the Spanish dictator's actions in full swing, in 1937 it became increasingly apparent even to the pacifist-minded in Britain that the war clouds were gathering once more over Europe. 'I think it's shameful the way England has allowed all this to happen,' Ken Watson said to his wife, Lucy.

They were sitting over breakfast in their Caversham semi-detached, Ken was digesting the newspaper, when he spoke out. Although Ken was angry, Lucy was really more frightened. She remembered the stories told by her parents and that mind-scarring First World War was only 19 years in the past. He looked up again from the paper and said, without any intention of drama, 'In my book its war before long!'

That was the end of the conversation, Ken looked at the clock on the mantelpiece and said, 'I must be off.' He worked for his father in the ladies hairdressing salon in the pleasant suburb of the big county town – not quite the place where he would be able to continue a serious debate with the customers.

Although to Ken it did seem that politicians were not prepared to recognise that Britain might again be drawn into a maelstrom with Germany, the events were not un-noticed by certain members of the Government, the Home Office, and leaders of industry.

The intimidation of countries by the Luftwaffe and its trained aircrews – well practised by bombing in Spain – cowering them into submission, was causing real concern. Frontiers no longer meant anything. The English Channel could be crossed in minutes – every citizen would be in the 'front line'.

As Ken snipped away and made small talk with his ladies, the thoughts would not go out of his mind. In London the thoughts were not going away either, plans were being completed for a fourth line of defence. It was to be called Air Raid Precautions, and later Civil Defence.

Idea for this fourth arm was to train large bodies of civilians – the worried people like Ken – into specialist units called Wardens, Decontamination squads (fear of gas being used was real), Rescue squads, First-Aid parties, and Auxiliary members of the Fire Services. The terrible devastation seen in Spain meant there would be light and heavy Rescue squads, to get out as many people as possible from ruins, working closely with the first-aiders.

But fire was also the big worry and, early in 1938, Ken was listening to the wireless when a Government appeal was made. It said, in essence, 'Men who feel themselves capable and can spare the time, should enrol in a new Auxiliary Fire Service!' Ken in his early 20's was within the age groups wanted.

Lucy knew immediately, as she looked over at her husband, what he wanted to do. He was a tall, fit man, always ready to express his view, and stand by it – except, of course, when being nice to dear old ladies in the salon! Just the type to be a willing volunteer.

When Ken reached the town's fire station, he soon found that he wasn't the only man who wanted to stand up and be counted. There was quite a queue. The training was only going to be a few hours, one evening and Sunday mornings! Handling such a response was a nightmare to the brigade's clerk-fireman. First in the queue was a man who had been enjoying an evening at the cinema when a message was flashed on the Vaudeville screen and he went straight round the corner to the fire station.

Mind you, Ken soon found his lack of confidence in the country's preparedness reinforced. The traditional Dennis fire engine, with its wheel escape ladder, gleamed red with polish and reflections of brightly shining brass, but it did look several years old. Not nearly so old as the machine manoeuvred tightly into the corner. That looked as though it had been there when the corrugated roofed building was put up! Neither had even a windscreen nor any weather protection.

But there was good cheer: the Home Office was organising the manufacture of a huge supply of trailer fire pumps, large and small, ready for a feared conflagration. These were to be issued to special stores as fast as they could be made, ready for the multitude of large and small fire services, which protected towns and villages across the country. 'Didn't I hear that Pulsometer – famous for its massive industrial pumps – is making fire pumps?' Ken mused.

'Let's have a go!' thought Ken, trying to discard his pessimism. 'Which of us has not felt a surge of excitement at the turn-out of the fire engine, with men clinging on by one hand while trying to dress with the other; with the gleaming bell clanging its insistent demand for right of passage.'

At the fire, lookers-on were always thrilled with admiration for the men as they jumped from the side seats before the machine stopped, ran out the hoses, pitched the escape ladder to the building, and got on with the job. Highly organised, efficient, but mused Ken, 'It's not going to be like that.'

How prophetic that thought was to prove to be. Perhaps in time that was what charged him to go on and lead men like himself – all kinds of civvy lives far removed from fire fighters, and those without any jobs at all – to help win the fire battles of the cities and towns, which saved Britain from defeat.

Forms collected at the fire station were completed and forwarded to the Corporation, the town's council. As Ken came out of the cramped one-storey building which served the fast-growing town, he smiled. It suddenly flashed across his mind that he was in The Butts, where, centuries before, folk gathered, required to exercise their skills as bowmen, to defend their country.

Sitting back and waiting was never the best way forward for Ken. But, at last, a letter came requesting that he report for drill on the following Thursday, at 7 pm.

*　　*　　*

What a mixture when the volunteers gathered – it was June 1938. At the fire station were pub landlords, draughtsmen, shop assistants, school teachers, engineers, hairdressers, car-salesmen, builders, a departmental store boss, an estate agent, a traveller selling lino, and an assistant bank manager, it seemed every trade known. Each man making it clear he was determined to give of his best to learn the mysteries of fire fighting. Gordon Castle was one of them – he had always wanted to be a fireman since he was a kid.

The evening passed quickly as all were shown and handled hoses, hydrant standpipes and keys, axes, ropes, all kinds of pieces of equipment. There was plenty to talk about as they made their way afterwards to a nearby hostelry, much favoured by the 'real' firemen – the 'brass hatted ones' as a wag tagged them as he supped his pint.

Already the AFS men felt a sort of attachment to each other. Ken wondered if they all recognised how hard he thought the work was to be. 'But it's going to be enjoyable, with this comradeship,' he quietly assured himself.

Over the pints, they all talked excitedly as they discussed that first night. It was voted 'the goods', and all looked forward to the next, a real drill.

It was better than expected when they returned to the station. The fire chief was an ex-Navy man – Russian convoys in the First World War – and they soon learned that he never minced words. 'Mount the fire engines,' he said. Everybody clambered up on to the wooden seats along the sides of the ladders – and hung on expecting to go racing away up the road.

The big doors were thrown open as Fire Chief Ernest Batchford pulled on his brass helmet and slid behind the wheel of RD 111, the newer engine, and they were off! But surprisingly it was very gentle. For the regular firemen watching, the 'brass hats' because of their metal helmets, it was the strangest sight they had seen. Their appliance was smothered with the volunteers, in their working clothes, about 15 hanging on to whatever they could frantically grasp.

The other engine, DP 741, or DP as they were soon to find out it was affectionately called, had been wriggled out of its corner, and was staggering along behind. It had earned its nickname because it was one of the family, it had been there so long! Indeed, it had solid tyres when it was new.

People in the street were amazed, they had never seen anything like it. Some of their shouted comments ridiculed the volunteers, which saddened Ken. But they all ignored it.

None of the new boys knew where they were heading but they soon smelt the answer. It was the Corporation yard, where cattle were slaughtered. Drill that night was assailed with all sorts of odours!

Dismounting, they were taught to line up, number, and form themselves into crews. The chief kept telling them how important it was to work together and look after each other. Next they were shown how to run out a length of hose.

It looked easy but soon proved not. Ken was early in the queue. 'Gosh, that's heavy,' he said to himself as he picked it up under his arm. As a hairdresser he hadn't the muscles of the likes of the brickies. So, using his brain to make up for brawn, he grasped the handles tightly and kept the roll absolutely upright. As he ran, the hose ran off perfectly. It was a good start.

Each week Ken and the others returned to the smells of the abattoirs. But everyone was too involved to worry. As the volunteers progressed through their drills a healthy rivalry sprang up. Each striving to better the next, and beat his time.

'It's a healthy sign,' Ken told Lucy when telling her what had happened one evening. 'The men seem to be forming themselves into cliques from their own districts, and there's a good crowd from Caversham.'

Once the pattern of forming districts had established itself, each strove harder than ever to beat the others. It wasn't unhealthy because all were recognising that the world drama made it almost certain that this could be for real. If a man dropped a standpipe, kinked his hose, failed to make a good suction joint (which meant there would be no water!), Ken noticed that it wasn't repeated the next week for fear of letting down the district.

Writing up his diary, which he kept so carefully, Ken realised that the 60 hours of training allotted to training auxiliaries was nearly up. By that time it was said a man should be reasonably proficient, at least have enough aptitude to be a great help to the brigade if there were hostilities.

'I wonder,' he wrote, '60 hours is a mere nothing – I couldn't be a hairdresser in that time and surely fire fighting is a profession if you are to do it properly. Still practice makes perfect. Mind you, we are not getting any actual experience of real fires!'

That was worrying Ken. There was no way auxiliaries were being allowed to go to real fires. 'Perhaps that will change,' he added as an afterthought.

He was not disheartened. Like Ken, other volunteers were so keen on their new found 'hobby', that he would see the same faces at every drill, and these were being held four nights a week and Sunday mornings, using the red machines and their peacetime trailer pump.

Fire Chief Batchford announced, 'We have one of the Home Office new pumps to test. Tomorrow evening we will take it to the lake and find out its capabilities.' There was great excitement as the grey trailer was hitched on and off went the AFS and some of the 'brass hats'.

Everything went well, Ken helped to make sure the unwieldy lengths of suction hoses were well coupled up so there was no delay in pumping water to the two jets, which put up an impressive picture of real power. 'Someone has done a good job designing this pump,' said Ken to the operator.

Suddenly, the sense of pleasurable achievement ended as a message arrived of a fire in the town. Ken could feel his adrenalin running in a way he had never known before, as, with the others, he scrambled to collect up the equipment. The trailer pump weighed nearly a ton and all were pulling and slipping, and some cursing, on the drag ropes as they pulled it 50 yards up a steep slope. 'We proved ourselves tonight,' he was to write later in his diary.

But first, hitching the pump behind the pump-escape, they flung themselves

21

aboard and, with bell clanging, raced off to the fire. The brass hats who had stayed behind with the other machine were already there.

Modestly the auxiliaries held back but curiosity took over. Walking up to the policemen who were holding back the crowd, Ken found that the magic word 'AFS' gained them instant admission to the building. Spotted by the Fire Chief they were given their first practical lesson.

'Come over here,' he said standing amongst the smoke. The first whiff was enough to make Ken and the others cough and splutter. But not to disgrace themselves, they stayed put and tried to convince themselves that they too were 'smoke eaters'.

As the fire came under control, Ken shivered and realised that others around him were too. Still in their civvies, wet from perspiration of pushing the pump up the slope and riding fast on the open fire engine – because there were no uniforms to be issued – the chill had set in. Ken wrote again in his diary, 'We refused to complain. It was good to get the experience. Others are jealous not to have had the chance.'

*   *   *

Word travelled fast that there was to be another night of special training. Nearly every man turned up for 'Escape work', rescuing people with the aid of the wheeled ladder. Volunteers were again hanging on the red pump-escape as it wound its way through the town centre to the Abbey Gateway. The centuries-old gatehouse is all that remains intact of the famous 12th century Benedictine Abbey reduced to ruins after Henry VIII dissolved the monasteries. Poetic, thought Ken, this was here the last time that England really saw war on her own soil, and landmarks in towns and cities were reduced to rubble!

'It is 40 feet high, thank goodness we at least know how to get the escape off the machine,' said Ken to his slightly nervous neighbour, clutching tightly to the brass rail to avoid being thrown off. The grunt in reply made it quite clear that knowing just how far the top of the gateway was from the ground hadn't made that man feel any less jittery.

The fellow on his other side, a bricklayer, said, 'I bet very few have ever climbed a ladder. Did you know that the rungs on an escape are further apart than the ordinary small ladder?' 'No,' said Ken. 'And they call them rounds not rungs,' said the man used to climbing, who was glad to have a chance to show his knowledge.

The regulars, the 'brass hats', were there to assist. The trouble was so was a big crowd. 'How the hell did they get to hear,' grunted Ken. 'Why don't they come and join?' Persuading people to sign on was still proving tough despite the publicity started by the Home Office in the autumn of 1937.

The Fire Chief told them before starting out, 'We shall slip the escape, wheel it into the building, wind it up, and bring a man down in approved fireman fashion.' He didn't say what that was, or how one held a person, in approved fashion.

The rivalry among the different districts was showing up as everyone gathered round to watch as the first team tilted the ladder off the engine and wheeled it to the Gateway brickwork, winding and extending the ladder at the same time. There was

22

a scramble for the honour of being first man up, and some friendly jostling before their new discipline took control.

All but a few volunteers were soon up on the roof, gazing around the town from an unusual and unexpected viewpoint. Some strode about with apparent nonchalance, while many were trying hard not to look over the edge! One or two, including the bricklayer, were daring to hang over the edge to see how small the people were below.

On the ground, the few who hated heights, looked a bit disconsolate. 'Don't worry,' said the nervous one, on the fire engine, to the man standing beside him. 'There are plenty of tasks we will do better than them. What do you do at work?' 'I'm an engineer.' 'Good, I'm a motor mechanic. We will make the best pair of pump operators in the town.'

Up the ladder strode the Fire Chief. 'When you carry anyone down, do not carry more than your own weight' he said. 'This is how you step off a building on to a ladder.' A couple of demonstrations of lifting a body over his shoulder; he turned picking up one of the men before he could say a word, stepped on to the ladder and carried him down to the ground!

The habitual joking and chaffing suddenly stopped. The remaining men gazed at each other, clearly summing each other up in a different light.

They paired off, and the first two were soon over the top. From the moment Ken went over the edge with a 'pal' over his shoulder he realised, as did all the others, they were doing something serious. One slip would have disastrous consequences, for the carrier as well as the carried.

Every man came down whole. 'Back up again and swop over,' said the Fire Chief. It was a moment Ken was going to remember for the rest of his life. All the districts were prepared to agree that the honours were even that night, and all had some men with no head for heights.

The pints of 'wallop' were going down well after that excitement when the buzz started that on the next exercise night they were to go to the River Thames for 'wet drill'. All drills, apart from the lake visit, had been 'dry', going through the motions without pumping water.

Clearly big efforts were being made to teach these men – just in case ... But to the 'brass hats' they were very much a bunch of amateurs, and to be kept away from the real fire engines, and real fires. Many, country-wide, were worried that they could lose their jobs. A fireman's job in the harsh depressive 30s was special, often only to be achieved through dead men's shoes – and so many men were joining the AFS that they were clearly outnumbered.

*   *   *

On the river bank the new Coventry Climax pump from the Home Office was set up. The suction hose was connected and dropped into the Thames, and lengths of hose run out and nozzles – 'Branches they're called,' screamed one of the regulars as he shuddered at an innocent's description – snapped on.

This was a moment when everyone felt proud, and glad to be getting to grips with the real equipment. In turn each man learnt how to use the controls and 'prime the pump' – lift the water from the river to send it under pressure to fight a fire. Every minute it could send 500 gallons on its way.

Those heavy brass branch pipes soon proved difficult to hold against the water pressure. 'They're lethal if you lose control,' shouted the Fire Chief. 'Break your jaw, at least,' in his usual laconic way. 'Lean your body forward, keep your feet firm, and grip it tight.'

There was something like 75 lbs pressure per square inch going through the branch, recalled Ken from his books. When it was his turn he remembered being told that if it got away it was like a snake, thrashing wildly, and could bust an arm or smash a skull!

He had just handed over his branch when, a new operator on the pump, in the excitement of the training, opened the throttle suddenly and the fun started! Out of control went the two branches, the men hanging on were scattered in all directions. One fell flat on the ground and, as he tried to get up, the powerful jet of water hit his backside. He went sprawling again, drenched to the skin.

Spectators were soon soaked as well. A 14-stone heavyweight threw himself on to the leaping, thrashing hose, only to be jerked about like a child. More men then piled on to both hoses and the pump operator closed his throttle. The hoses subsided like dead things, leaving drenched auxiliaries spread-eagled in all directions. 'My own bloody clothes mucked up again,' cursed the half-choking man next to Ken.

It was all over in about seven or eight seconds. Some were for murdering the poor pump operator, others for chucking him in the river, but it was all good humoured. Ken said, 'We really have learnt something tonight.' Curses and jokes mingled in the replies.

'Wet or not,' said another, as they packed up the equipment, 'I am definitely going on to the Aldershot Tattoo.' 'Bloody fool,' said another. 'No,' said Ken, 'It will be those who just keep watching us who will be the bloody fools.'

Although Ken was right in his feeling that many of the idle-watchers looked upon them as grown-up kids playing with water, there were others slowly making the decision to join up. 'Christ that was a shambles really,' said Ken when John Lander, a neighbour from the next street, who like Ken was one of the originals, came into the hairdressing shop. 'I still think we are in for war; I wonder how long we have got?

'It's those gawkers who get my goat, they seem to bury their heads at the thought!' 'And they don't realise how much time we're putting into training, or the clothes we are ruining,' replied John, with feeling.

*   *   *

Rumours began to persist that as auxiliaries were, at long last, to be issued with some sort of uniform or overalls. Ken and his Caversham district pals were all measured one Tuesday evening at the fire station in The Butts. Great excitement:

'Perhaps they are taking us for real,' said Ken to John. 'We shall see,' was all he got for a reply.

When the kit did eventually arrive, the atmosphere was much more enthusiastic, everyone was jumping around like young school-boys in a first set of long trousers. Everyone except Alec that was.

The overalls were blue dungaree material with a badge on the left breast, AFS, in red letters with the name of their town, READING, underneath. Also issued were thick webbing belts with chromium buckles, shiny axes and pouches, rubber boots and peak caps.

Everyone felt so smart that each seemed to grow a couple of feet as they tried on the equipment. Except Alec Hunt. He was 6 ft 7 in tall and he was doubled up to his ankles as he tried to get into his overalls. The 'bottom' came about the knees and the sleeves nearly reached his elbows!

The tailor seeing 6 ft 7 in had clearly thought it should be 5 ft 7 in and had made the garment accordingly! 'We all nearly died of laughing,' Ken told his wife when he got home. He was feeling not only proud but, much more vital, that some one at last was agreeing with him that the AFS was important. Basic the overalls might be, but they certainly helped to protect the men's own clothes, few were likely to be earning more than £2 10s a week, if that much.

Proficiency increased rapidly as the men trained. A large number were buying books out of their own pockets, subjects such as knots and lines, hydraulics, and all the ARP pamphlets, in their eagerness. 'Do you realise,' said Ken, over a beer after a hard evening's training, 'our hours at drills and lectures are far in excess of the Government's allotted time?'

Ken was aware of the worries of the regular firemen that the bursting enthusiasm was causing. He could sense a growing problem. The council employees, whose jobs and pay relied on them turning out at all hours when there was a fire, were making it plain they were not too keen on teaching Ken and his fellow auxiliaries the finer points of fire fighting.

'I can understand it,' said Ken, when some of the auxiliaries started to gripe at unhelpful tactics. 'Anyway if there is a war, fire fighting is going to be very different! The best thing to do is learn technical books.' Clearly Ken was being recognised as one of the leaders, and quite a few went off to do the same, knowing he was mugging up as much as he could.

It didn't take long before this enthusiastic bunch found their excessive hours of attendance at drills and lectures was recognised. The Fire Chief told them, 'You can report on Saturday nights, from 7 pm to 10.30 pm and ride to fires with the professionals.'

It was a big moment, everyone was experiencing a feeling of pride. They had reached the stage when they were recognised. 'We've shown the Fire Chief we can be relied on,' said Ken. He was talking to a group of the Caversham chaps – it was strange how the districts seemed to have grouped up.

There was a lot more men now, numbers swelled as they were seen drilling so wholeheartedly. 'There's a sense of patriotism growing,' said Ken, 'and probably

25

they would like to have a basinful of what we have been doing.' 'But how the hell can we train with all these numbers?' asked John.

The Fire Chief also realised the training was getting beyond the capabilities of one man. Trailer pumps were being delivered by the Home Office. Events meant that times were changing fast. He mustered the men. 'Volunteers will be split up into their respective districts in the town, East, West, Central and South Reading, and Caversham. The man in charge of each district will be one of the early volunteers. They will be responsible to me for general training and behaviour.'

He listed the leaders, ending, 'Caversham, Ken Watson.' It was clearly a great honour and Ken felt very proud, and then a little scared. The men from the separated suburb north of the Thames gathered round him. 'We're with you, congratulations,' said John. The others were all murmuring their approval, it was clearly a popular appointment. 'But I bet we are going to work bloody hard!' added John.

'Too right; where are we going to do our training?' asked Ken. That started a lot of chatter. Caversham was mainly an area of houses and no obvious potential meeting place came to mind. They decided to stay at the Corporation highways' yard. 'All the others will be moving out to their districts, and its only over the river bridge for us.'

'One snag' said John. 'There is nowhere we can keep a trailer pump at the yard.' 'We shall have to fetch one from the Butts fire station, until we can sort ourselves out,' replied Ken.

Ken was full of his ideas when he arrived home to tell his wife. 'Aren't there any women involved?' she asked. 'No, it is still being run very much like a man's game, unlike the other ARP services.' His father was also concerned when Ken went to the salon. 'Can you manage to do both jobs?' he asked. 'I will have to,' said Ken, 'I'm not being paid by the AFS.'

His father's concern was quite right. Drills went ahead very regularly under the new conditions. It was a great load for Ken, and the other 'amateurs' responsible for training. Having planned the programme ahead, Ken then sat down to organise lectures and topical talks, in case an evening should turn wet. The learner was now the teacher. How few people realised that so much now relied on the auxiliaries.

Ken kept a drill register. He was delighted at the response, everyone was turning up as often as humanly possible, and he told the men. 'It is fixed also for us to go to the police station in Valpy Street for lectures by experts on explosives – talks on bombs, cannon shells, and craters formed by bombs!' He let the second part of the sentence, which he had carefully added, sink in. The men were already well aware of Hitler's latest moves. 'Bloody hell!' said someone in the back row. 'Could be,' replied Ken.

5 · Black out test

MUNICH! The 1938 crisis was beginning to develop. More men were quickly knocking at the door of the town's fire station, wanting to join the auxiliaries. When Chamberlain flew back from meeting Hitler, waving his piece of paper declaring peace was saved, Reading's AFS had grown to several hundred strong.

Training reached a new crescendo in the weeks leading up to that dramatic moment. Ken Watson was trying hard to cope with all the extra problems. John Lander, and the other originals, were all doing their best to help. 'These new men really have the feeling that something is going to happen,' said Ken. The war clouds were certainly black.

'They feel this could be their testing time. Why on earth else would they go on training even in the dark?' replied John. 'They're doing their best to be perfect,' said Ken.

He sat down at the make-shift table-cum-desk in the tiny wooden sales office of a new housing estate which had become their 'home'. Some months earlier vigilant combing of any likely place to set up a station in Caversham had paid off when this was found. The high walls of sandbags surrounding what was literally no more than a very large shed showed how hard they had worked to make it possible as a headquarters.

The Balmore Drive housing estate was unfinished, and a garage in a nearby empty house was pressed into service to house their first trailer pump, ladders, standpipes, and other gear. But at least it was in the centre of Caversham. Ken was delighted that he had persuaded the local builder, R J Haddock, to help them – his son was in the AFS.

Like his counterparts in the other suburbs, Ken was finding a fund of goodwill from local businesses. The Corporation wrote to many firms asking if they were public spirited enough to loan their lorries in the event of an emergency, to tow the Home Office trailer pumps.

Trailer pumps were now being delivered to Reading, as to all other towns – and many villages where AFS men had harmoniously joined forces with the traditional volunteer firemen. Six hundred pumps a week were being constructed, most pumps going into store for the present. There were still not enough to go round. Tom Goldsmid, a Jew, who had moved down from London to live and then joined the AFS, seemed to have a fund of contacts still in the capital. His latest rumour, 'In London there are no pumps for the AFS, the regulars are using all those supplied so far!' he told his new pals.

Ken and John were studying the details about their own pump. It was the smallest of the two sizes, called a light pump. 'It can output 100 to 120 gallons per minute – the major can shift 500 gallons,' Ken added, as an after thought, as he flicked the details. He was trying to solve a problem.

'Of course, the boys are eager to work on the major pump, but it's better to train on the light ones – and they do some useful work,' replied John, who had been appointed his second in command.

'Here it is, look at the drawing,' said Ken. 'That belt drive from the engine to the primer is bound to get wet in that position, that's why it slips and why we couldn't raise water.' John studied the drawing, 'We must tell operators to try and keep it dry.' He looked again, 'And we're going to go on getting bruised knuckles, there is no way to modify those controls.'

'They are not well placed,' agreed Ken, 'but with that streamlining it really looks a smasher. Especially with the brasso and elbow grease of the men.' 'They certainly are proud of it – and who bought the brasso? You did,' said John.

'I'll tell you one thing,' said Ken, ignoring the last remark, if we hadn't been promised a lorry, the men would pull that trailer pump round with their own hands!'

Suddenly, the day came when the Prime Minister returned from Munich with the 'good news'. People sighed with relief. As the tension eased so the AFS changed again. 'Do you know that the volunteers in town have dropped to below 50 per cent,' Ken told his faithful followers. 'But, not one of the early volunteers has quit!'

There was some embarrassed shuffling of feet, 'We hadn't thought of it like that,' said one. 'Thanks, it's the same across the town,' he replied.

'One thing will be easier, all that intensive training you have had with your gas masks on is over – at least for now! No more marching or doubling 'till you feel at home!' (that was the catch phrase of the Fire Chief), climbing ladders, running hose, pulling the trailer pump, with them on.' There was a cheer: the way his words had pictured their suffering and sweating, brought home what they had begun to take for granted.

'With the crisis over, the gasmasks will go into a central store.'

Talking together afterwards John said, 'If that's 1938, roll on 1939 – and let us hope things sort themselves out quickly.' 'With trenches dug and gas masks given to civilians, I still reckon we're just lucky to have a bit more time,' said Ken.

Early in 1939, four outstanding events went into Ken's diary. 'We were measured at the station for our fire-fighting kit and when these were delivered we went into the seventh heaven of delight,' he wrote. 'We didn't join for the sake of a uniform, but now it's delivered we have gained official status and recognition.

'As regards fit, they are splendid and the texture of the cloth is superb.' Later in the war years, he was to remember that often. The standard was never to be repeated in full-time service. He was also to remember his added comment, 'No waterproof leggings, or overcoats, the Fire Chief says 'Firemen are tough and don't need them'.' So Reading saved that expense.

The next special note in the diary was the presentation by the Government of a silver lapel badge, to be worn in civvies, emblazoned in scarlet lettering with AFS. All firemen who had completed the official 60 hours training received it. The presentation took place at the Town Hall, and was made by Wing Commander Hadsell.

'We paraded at the town's tiny fire station in full fire fighting kit, complete with steel helmets, and marched, bursting with pride, to the Town Hall. We were joined by the other ARP units who had been progressing as favourably as us.

'The Fire Service really excelled themselves that night. For once the public could only gaze and pass no comment.'

Ken was especially pleased with the way his Caversham men had shown themselves. He was generous to think that all the other district leaders must be feeling the same. But soon there was an even greater pleasure, he was to meet the King and Queen.

*   *   *

As the weeks passed swiftly it was clear, with the spectacular rallies and bombastic noises from the Nazi's leader, that the war clouds were gathering again. The men realised this. Training developed even more strenuously. Ken's own ideas, from what he had learnt in London, and reading his books, was really widening their experience.

A few extra volunteers arrived from time to time, after a few hours training at the central fire station. 'I'm right glad to see you,' said Ken, with real sincerity. 'When the time comes, we are going to need every man!' He had made up his mind that war was coming a long time before, but quite definitely on that June day when Prime Minister Neville Chamberlain spoke to the House of Commons of his anxieties for Poland.

Ken also remembered older 'locals' of the Royal Berkshire Regiment telling him of the immense field gun bombardment executed by the Germans just 21 years before, in their final and almost successful push to break the Allies in the First World War. That had been planned with great precision, not only with high explosives but clouds of killing gas!

Gas might well be used again, in his mind, whatever the League of Nations might say. Gasmasks were re-issued. They were no terror for his men. Toughened from the running and drills in them, they had got used to the encumbrance.

Seven seconds was the average time it took them to get their masks on when Ken shouted, 'GAS!'. Regularly he picked the worst moment. With the mask and breathing cylinder in its haversack strapped to the chest, and with a length of hose held high to one side – so that it would unroll and not tangle with the mask's case – his urgent shout would stop the drill. Steel helmets would be pushed back, respirators ripped out of the case and put on, helmets on, hose picked up and on the move again, far quicker than you can read this verbal drill routine.

That was the easy version. Sometimes Ken would give his men drills in gas clothing – to beat the skin penetrating versions – that made them sweat and curse. 'The men look like Martians,' he told John when they were having another of their critical discussions. He was right, oilskin jackets and trousers pulled on top of their uniforms, again with the gasmask in the alert position on the chest, and a oilskin hood on the helmet to cover the neck, and similar gauntlets, marrying up with their rubber boots, made firemen and other ARP members look strange – and very worrying to those ex-Servicemen who remembered the last time!

'You're right,' replied John, 'the thought of gas bombs from planes is enough to frighten me. It's tough on the men, too, it's so exhausting, with nowhere for the body heat to escape. I know they would be dead if there was a hole for the gas to get in.

'The great thing is there has never been a word of complaint, despite all the grunts and groans. They realise they are as ready as humanly possible, but most of the people in the country don't seem to be,' said Ken.

'Why rubber boots, not leather like the brass hats?' 'Because they can be boiled to neutralise the gas, leather cannot,' tartly replied Ken, not realising that John was simply dodging him starting to put the politicians to rights once again.

'You're right about the men,' said Ken. 'They are still all volunteers, they don't have to sweat and tire themselves out unless they wish. Thank God they do, why do so many others still laze at home?'

The drills were carried out for two hours, three evenings a week, plus three hours on Sunday mornings. Ken, and his opposite numbers, across the country, had a right to be pleased.

'I bet when the bombing starts, many will still grouse and dodge doing even a few hours to try and save our towns,' he said prophetically.

*   *   *

The King and Queen reviewed the great ARP Rally in Hyde Park, in June, 1939. Ken was there, with two others from his Caversham station. Contingents came from every conceivable part of England and Wales. 'It was an unforgettable sight to us as well as the thousands of Londoners watching,' he described, on his return. Heads of all civil defence organisations were there with the Royal family. 'It was amazing the way people thronged to the park to see us all march past.'

Tremendous as that special parade was, with all its recognition of the importance of their hours of voluntary effort, there was another bonus. Immediately it was over, Ken was among the many firemen who did not head straight for home. They wended their way to the headquarters of the London Fire Brigade.

'We were made to feel quite at home at this most modern of fire stations,' he related. 'We had to satiate our thirst!' Big words, and there were some puzzled looks as Ken, showed his excitement. But as he, and the other two lucky chaps, told about the turntable ladders, emergency tenders, breakdown wagons ... , the rest were just as excited – all were ignorant, as Reading, like many other towns, did not boast such equipment.

They were vivid in their detail of the first-hand viewing. 'We have gathered some useful information and tips, and we must put these to good use at our own station.' It was prophetic thinking, coming at a time when the Prime Minister was making a frank admission that Britain's passive defences were 'far from complete'.

The excitement had hardly died down when an exercise was announced to cover the whole of Reading. 'Indeed the whole of the country, I believe, certainly the South East,' he briefed his men. 'It is to test black-out conditions. All ARP personnel will participate. Primary functions are to see how ARP workers can react to a blackout, and how other people do, especially drivers.'

Suddenly, at a given hour, the streets of Reading, and Caversham where Ken and his team watched, were plunged into complete darkness. a total blackout was a breathtaking new experience for the country. It had a strange effect on everybody – and clearly was going to add a thrill to the evening's work which was ahead.

Comparing notes afterwards, Ken agreed with the others, much valuable information had been gained. The exercise presumed that war had been declared and enemy planes were raiding! The blackout was the signal that the alert had sounded.

Ken's firemen dressed in their full kit, gasmasks strapped to their chests, steel helmets replacing the peaked caps, scrambled to their cars, taxis, and borrowed lorries, and hitched the pumps on behind. 'Remember the contact points,' he shouted. 'If a raid should start fires, policemen and wardens will intercept you at those spots and direct you to the incident.'

When the 'red alert' was given they set off at seven minute intervals following the set patrol route, planned to cover their area. The same routine was happening all over the town. The theory was that a warden could always find a fire engine in seven minutes.

Ken was unhappy about the theory but, then, he was so often critical of the established thinking. It was the early hours of the morning when the exercise ended. Talking privately with John after it was over, he exclaimed, 'What's the matter with the powers-that-be, it's not going to work! On paper it sounds good but not in practice. If the firemen find a blaze themselves they're going to stop, and nobody's going to meet the warden.

'As officer-in-charge of the station I am not going to know where any of my pumps are. If the bombers hit a factory or foodstore my crews, instead of fighting that for the war effort, are going to be trying to save a private house, or something like that!'

From his anger, it was clear that Ken could see that the system was not going to change.

Containing his outburst, Ken then agreed, 'The system worked well tonight. But, that was only because the few fires were bonfires, and there was rivalry to get to them. How those clowns who caught up the other crew, and then both went hell-for-leather to get there first, avoided an accident, I will never know. At least they were good humoured enough to 'drown' themselves as well as the spectators.'

In came the drivers of the 'borrowed' lorries with notes of the mileage travelled. 'Petrol and oil has been replaced,' reported one of his volunteers. 'Tomorrow night we will all be back to clean the hose and equipment – tonight I mean,' he added, suddenly realising the time. There was no shirking, these were real volunteers.

*   *   *

Behind that blunt, basic approach to fire-fighting, Fire Chief Ernest Batchford knew all about survival. The older AFS men could recognise the special ribbon he wore – the Meritorious Service Medal. He well remembered the first World War.

Just two years after he joined the Gloucester part-time volunteer fire brigade – when no one could guess that he would become a Freeman of that City – and 14 days after the 1914 war was declared, he joined the Royal Navy. It was in the Navy, always so closely coupled with the fire services of those days, that his distinguished service in Russia was recognised.

Returning home, a warrant officer, RN, he joined Reading's brigade as a fireman-driver. Appointed a sub-engineer the next year, he became second officer in 1927. Right until 1939 the chief constable of the town was also the chief fire officer, although 'Batchy' was recognised as the fire chief.

Then, with another war coming, and the changed legislation, Mr Batchford became chief officer. Perhaps he could remember the incredible way Britain had put together its Navy to fight the first time? Could he see it all happening again?

Whatever? Before the total blackout exercise, he was making special plans. Landlords of the pubs around The Butts fire station belonged to the AFS and knew the men well. Barrels of beer and crates of other wallop were delivered. Drinking on the station was not a practice, this was something special.

It was clearly the end of an era, his new role, a new fire engine and fire station coming very soon. Things were never going to be the same again. When the official exercise ended, and the men returned to the station, the night started. It was a party for this one occasion, a black out in more senses for some.

In no time after that he was declared district officer to try and bring together the independent brigades of the towns, and villages around. He would be trying to liaise with places like Henley, Mortimer, Pangbourne, Sonning, and Wokingham – all places used to working very much on their own. All across the country other fire officers were also achieving the first instincts of joint preservation. Something for which the blitzed towns were to feel unbelievably grateful but, again, no one knew that then!

*   *   *

By July, with tension growing all around, some men were beginning to feel down-hearted. For months they had the misfortune, or 'bad-luck', to miss a real fire call of any description. After spending so many hours on hard training and learning the job, there seemed, to them, no chance to put into practice what they had learnt.

Ken was worried about this and decided to mock-up a big fire on the training ground, where they could all get some action. 'Let's really go to town,' he told John. 'Do it big!' And do it! they did.

Twenty feet high, 15 feet in diameter, when the firemen finished building the bonfire it was a solid affair. Tree trunks and branches were collected from a site where a large number of trees were being felled. Forty gallons of old engine oil was then poured over the lot and left to soak until the next drill night.

All the men turned up again and excitement was running high as their fire pumps were set into one of the new 'dams', portable canvas water containers which were now being issued. These were being filled with water from lines of hose running from hydrants, some distance off. It was showing them how fires could be fought, even if the local mains water services were disrupted.

All waited expectantly for the whistle. Ken inserted three practice incendiary bombs at the base of the bonfire. Then, when the flames were really roaring, Ken blew his whistle for 'get to work'.

Five crews jumped to it. All wanted to be the first with 'water on'. It was one of the hottest nights of the year and the men in their heavy tunics were soon soaked to the skin with their exertions. Their positions surrounded the fire and, with all the jets trained on the fire, firemen on the opposite side were receiving a showerbath. Some of it was bound to happen when fighting a blaze from all sides but, the innocent expressions from their 'oppos', as if it was all an accident, was too good to be true.

Instinctively the men straightened out into two lines, flung off their heavy tunics and, shouting 'More pressure' proceeded to set about each other with powerful jets of water! In a few seconds every man was soaked to the skin, they all oozed water, but nobody flinched. As the jets knocked the men over like skittles, they scrambled back to their feet to join in again. Steel helmets went flying, specs were knocked off, and then dramatically the whistle blew for 'Knock off'.

'Knock off, that's just about the most appropriate order in the fire service,' laughed John. 'I don't know what the chief officer would say but that's the best thing that's happened since it all started,' replied Ken.

He was right, so many evenings had been spent by the men in voluntary training that they had gradually built to a pitch of excitement, which needed some action. It dispelled the growing irritation.

'Nothing is more exciting than fighting with a live, charged hose kicking in your hands,' went on Ken. 'Their exuberance found an outlet – with themselves as the target. Nobody has been hurt.'

When the men collected up all the gear, soaked as they were, they volunteered to take it back to the Central Fire Station. 'Don't bump into the chief officer,' thought Ken. He didn't really care, he was so pleased that the niggling was washed away.

*   *   *

Ken was planning ahead with ideas for more training when he turned to John and said, 'Why don't we run another of those big prepared fires and really see just how good they are at trying to put it out? Let's do it without the men knowing anything about it; go as if to a real fire?'

Clandestine was the word for it; Ken and John called on a car breaker they knew a couple of miles away near Caversham Mill. He laughed his head off, one of his big worries always was that if the site caught alight it would be hellish trying to put it out. 'I'll build you one,' he said, 'but its going to take you a long time to put it out!' he was quite sure of that, and even more so as he got his men to heap up old car bodies, oil, petrol, and tyres.

When he finished he told Ken, 'You really are going to have a long and dirty job

– I hope you can keep it under control.' As he added that flippant remark, he suddenly felt a bit worried, 'Can your AFS handle it?' Quick as a flash Ken replied, 'Our boys are good.' The car dealer did not look very reassured by the confidence.

When the telephone rang in the sandbagged wooden hut giving the alarm, the men manning the first unit to go out dashed to their borrowed lorry and raced off dragging their light pump behind them. The fire was really blazing as they arrived. And the water supply was a long way away. Immediately, John, who was in charge, telephoned back a message for another pump – 'It would be necessary to pump water from the River Thames,' he said. He ignored the hydrant because this created what was to be expected in a typical wartime situation.

Quickly the second pump arrived at the river, the hoses were run from the pump to the other pump – which had set itself up half way to the fire – and had its hoses to as near the fire as heat would allow the men to get.

Ken and the car dealer stood back and watched. Suddenly, the hose came alive as the water sped through, wriggling. With a loud crackling the water spurted out and into the fire. With all their training, the men kept their cool and knew just where to direct the water. Petrol, oil, and tyres, make a perfect fire cocktail, especially with the intense heat and choking black fumes swirling around. Expertly the men put up a wall of water, cutting off the oxygen, and the fire was doused quickly, and skilfully.

The dealer pushed out his hand to shake with Ken. 'And you're sure these men aren't professionals?' That was a compliment Ken appreciated. It was also the start of a long and valuable friendship, although at that stage Ken did not realise how valuable. The spares and metal the dealer found for the worn-out vehicles, to keep them running, solved many a headache, which other stations faced without such a good friend.

*   *   *

War is coming soon. Listening to the wireless, and reading the newspapers with the reports of the debates in Parliament, somehow his gut feeling told Ken nothing would stop Hitler after the invasion of Austria and Czechoslovakia last year.

At the end of July, after an evening's drill, he called the men together. 'How many would volunteer for full-time service in the event of hostilities?' Immediately more than a dozen stepped forward and gave their names. Most of the others said, 'We would like to but our jobs are going to be important to the war effort.'

One or two had no desire to serve full-time, but 'We will attend whenever possible,' was the chorused reply.

He called the new volunteers together and talked it through. 'Immediately hostilities break out, report to this Action Station.' That was the title which had been given to the dispersal buildings in the various suburbs.

It didn't take long, Hitler was threatening Poland, 'France and Britain seem poles apart,' Ken told Lucy, his wife, 'And I'm not trying to be funny. And now Russia is siding with Hitler!' He shook his head. For her, and his work as a ladies' hairdresser, the world seemed equally upside down. Mind you, her neighbour's husband had already been recalled as a Navy reservist back in July, so, like Ken, she was expecting it.

Dawned the fateful September 1st. As soon as the news came over the wireless at 10.30 am that the Germans were entering Poland, the men acted. There was no question of waiting until war was declared. Literally dropping everything they were doing, they raced to their stations all over the town. Ken picked up the telephone and reported to the Central Fire Station. 'Caversham Action Station' is standing by.'

The day buzzed with events, as they listened to a wireless, while they checked and re-checked their prized equipment. Prized it was, because they knew that a lot more was still needed across the country to give the AFS the tools with which to fight.

Cinemas, the town's dog stadium, Ascot racecourse, and all other public entertainments were immediately closed by Government order, to prevent one bomb killing hundreds of innocent civilians at a time. 'What about the Derby?' said one of the men, who had laid a ante-post bet. He was right, that caused quite a furore and later, quietly without any publicity, the Derby was allowed to be run. 'What about petrol, its going to be rationed to six or eight gallons a month,' said another.

Evacuation of children from the cities saw crocodiles of children – and tears. Special trains carried them out, so, too, did the red London double-decker buses to be seen rushing across the countryside far from their regular routes.

That night the blackout exercise became reality. No street lights, no shops' illuminations, every house made sure its blackout curtains let no chinks of light show. The ARP wardens were out and about on duty, like the firemen. Every time someone forgot and opened a door, the shout could be heard echoing, 'Shut that door!'

Overhead a solitary plane droned. Very few below knew how pleased the country's leaders were when the pilot reported the blackout's success. War had come to Britain. For the first time everybody was in the front line – the first time for 300 years.

6 · Action stations

Feverish activity took place from the moment the men became full-time members of the Auxiliary Fire Service. Commandeered lorries arrived for towing the pumps, and these were piled high with equipment and the pumps hitched on the back in readiness. Well-known firm's names were finding a new experience: Sollys, Cannon, McCarthy Fitts. Sawyer had two lorries, so Ken Watson let him keep one. It was the same all over the town and country.

Major task when that was done was to make a real solid protection job of sandbagging the Action Station. 'We have got the sandbags, we will have to fill them with earth,' said Ken. 'Let's get on with it.' The filling went on without pause. Everybody had been led to believe that when war did break out, bombing would start immediately.

'The lack of preparation everywhere is appalling,' Ken said quietly to John Lander, as they took their turn to pause for a cup of tea. 'So much seems to have been left undone, it's as if people half-hoped for a second Munich.'

One of the firemen came up. 'Sir, We are going to need hundreds of filled bags if we are going to make an earth wall round this estate office blast proof. I have an idea, can I go and make a contraption to fill six at a time?' And he did, such was the spirit.

How they all sweated as they shovelled the earth into and tied the bags, carried, and tamped them down all around the wooden building. There was assistance from the part-timers arriving for the weekend and in the evenings, willing and eager to help. 'All this for less than three quid a week,' quipped one of the new full-time men. 'And nothing for us,' grunted the part-timer next to him. There was no bad feeling, money was the last thing on their minds.

'What can we find to protect the roof from shrapnel?' asked Ken. That proved much more difficult to overcome but, eventually, after a great deal of 'trouble', corrugated iron sheets 'arrived'. Fixed into position, and held down by more sandbags, it was the best they could do. They were as ready as possible.

Twelve men, plus Officer-in-charge Ken Watson, squeezed into a room intended to be big enough to do a deal to sell a new house. 'Duty hours will be 12 on and 12 off, but you must turn out from home on sirens,' briefed Ken. Day in and day out this was to go on – and, in addition, the part-timers were arriving for duty at every possible minute they could!

Everyone was tense. It was the same in the other Action Stations across the town, there were now six – and all over the rest of the country, presumed Ken. At least equipment being provided by the Government was coming through quicker.

36

Trailer pumps were being delivered in two sizes. The light pumps were capable of an output of 100 to 120 gallons of water a minute; the larger units – which became known as major pumps, and were eagerly sought after by crews – could shift up to 500 gallons in a minute.

Rumour was around that these would be reinforced later by an issue of self-propelled heavy units, each mounted on a lorry chassis. These, with a 27 horse-power engine, would deliver 700 to 900 gallons a minute. 'That would be a formidable and powerful weapon to face the bombers,' thought Ken. 'And quite a contrast to peacetime fire engines.'

By contrast the town's councillors were collecting a lot of flak, with their efforts to buy towing vehicles, 'cheap' in the view of the men.

None realised that the Treasury's permission, as recently as August, had been 'not to buy more than one car for every ten light trailer pumps'. In October it was changed to cover 'all first line pumps and fifty per cent of second'.

*   *   *

'Hilarious,' was how one of the 'brass hats' described the efforts to find vehicles to tow the Home Office pumps which were suddenly beginning to appear in numbers. 'The Government promised councils £5, saying they would pay half, towards each towing unit they bought.' Many councils clearly did not want to spend their own ratepayers' money by adding to that figure!

London-type taxis were prominent in towns. In Reading taxis came from Vincents, regular sights on the rank outside the main railway stations. Bought or commandeered, the firemen never could make up their minds, they simply cussed them. The few who could drive were used to driving cars and found difficulty struggling with the gate-crash gear changes on the offside of the driver.

All kinds of cars were pressed into service. At the Oxford Road station a Morris 10, JB2311, was the loving pride of Harold Sharp, the action station leader. Some well intentioned people were giving their cars. They could see there would be no petrol to drive them. Rationing was coming in days – six gallons a month for really essential users – and pinking 'Pool' petrol at that!

At Caversham there was no love lost on the 'Grey Ghost', another Morris saloon, which was issued to them. 'It must be the oldest they could find,' grunted Ken. There was virtually no compression on the engine. By the time it was fitted with a towing hitch and ladder rack on the roof, then loaded, it would just about progress along the flat roads – and there were not many of them in Caversham.

Fed up with the ribald remarks of people who watched them train, the AFS men were completely cheesed off when, going to a fire, they had to get out and push the 'Grey Ghost' up hill. No amount of protest could persuade the authority to change it. Every time it was taken away by the mechanics it sailed along – of course it did, they asked the firemen to take off all the kit.

One day, Ken was blowing his top, it was all so ridiculous. He refused to take the gear off, and said, 'Take it as it is, pump and all!' His insistence won the day. The mechanics were soon stranded trying to climb a hill – and the problem was solved.

As replacement, Ken was given a six-cylinder Packard, which had been used as a breakdown truck. It still had its impressive American saloon body at the front but, behind the front seat, the rest was cut off where it had been turned into a workhorse.

A powerful vehicle, it was going to be well used, decided Ken. His men dashed around scrounging timber and metal, so that it could be made to imitate a real fire engine. Lockers either side, to sit on, and a ladder rack above. Other stations were also endeavouring to copy the red machines in miniature. Everybody seemed to be dashing around trying to find bells to complete the illusion – one station even settled for a sheep bell.

Buicks, Packards, a Hudson Terraplane, Morris Isis, and other more powerful cars, started to flow into the central fire station, as Home Office 'guidance' made civic authorities realise the necessity.

*   *   *

Meanwhile similar, almost pantomime, efforts had been taking place in other towns to find vehicles to tow the new pumps. The new Fire Brigades Act was demanding that councils provide adequate fire protection and liaise with neighbours. Slough, in close-by Buckinghamshire – which had just made six retained firemen into a full-time team, as the war clouds thickened – bought six railway goods delivery vans.

They were Morris Commercials belonging to the Great Western Railway, but, broken down and stored on the trading estate! Mechanics and carpenters among the firemen were put to work. When they finished there were six smartly painted towing units, with engines running and complete with lockers. They looked smart but there were dubious shakes of the head.

'Will they do the job?' one of the workers asked his mechanic friend. Screwing up his face, the reply was, 'Time will tell.' As it did!

*   *   *

Evacuees from London were arriving in Reading by the trainload. The billeting of hundreds of children from the East End was still going ahead, frantically, on Sunday, September 3. There was a strange air of worry; everyone knew that Britain's ultimatum to Germany was running out and the Prime Minister was going to be speaking on the wireless at 11 am. Would Hitler pull back out of Poland? Nobody really thought he would.

Harold Randle was frantically busy, like thousands of other Scouts and Guides across the country, helping at the halls pressed into service to cope with finding 'safe' homes. Willing workers were rushed off their feet providing comfort, tea, and sandwiches or biscuits, to the pathetic, frightened young children. Most could hardly remember their own names it was all so awful. The only means of keeping their identity, were the labels tied to their clothes, as they clutched at the cardboard boxes of their gasmasks.

He was at St Mary Magdalen's Church Hall – 'How they need that lady,' he thought, himself at the tender age of 12, as he watched one wonderful woman. She was the perfect mother, trying to help them come to terms with a world so different from their Brixton – and probably as bewildering as any imagination of German bombers. His job was guiding the Mayor, in his car, delivering children to their new homes.

Gas attacks were much in people's minds and Harold suddenly found himself in the midst of a crisis. The Mayor realised his service respirator was missing from his car boot.

When it was described, Harold said, 'I know where I delivered that.' Un-knowingly, he had unloaded it with luggage belonging to the evacuees. Off he went on his cycle and recovered it. Little did he realise that soon he too would be carrying one everywhere.

As mid-morning approached Harold excused himself to go home. That natural cub reporter instinct, which was to be his future, was showing again. He wanted to hear for himself what Prime Minister Neville Chamberlain had to say to the nation on the wireless. It did not take long; in essence, 'The British second and final ultimatum to Germany to stop the war on Poland, given at 9 am, had been ignored, Britain was already at war,' said the Prime Minister.

Mum and Dad looked really worried. Dad rubbed his ankle, where he had been shot and taken prisoner in 1918 – one of 30 to survive when hundreds of the Devonshire Regiment died holding back a big final push. It was as if the quietly spoken war declaration had struck through to the tender spot.

Within minutes the sirens started wailing their warning. The two whole minutes they continued was frightening in itself as the note rose and fell. Naturally, everybody rushed outside to look at the sky, just the opposite to the civil defence planners' intentions.

Along the street came the Air Raid Warden. A short man he was trying to give himself the height of authority as he shouted, 'Get indoors, get off the streets!' All the fearsome stories of bombs and gas were brought to mind as he rushed along wrapped in strange yellow gas clothing, with his black helmet bobbing on top. It looked almost funny but, for the warden inside, it as not. Within no time at all he was suffering a soaking.

There was nothing to see in the sky and people disappeared. Harold realised that he was not going to be allowed to return to the church hall until the danger was past. Mum said, 'When will you be home?' He shook his head, 'I don't know, there are hundreds of people still down there. It's rotten for them – and the biscuits! Even the dogs wandering around won't eat them.'

It was not long before the level note of the All Clear started. Nothing had happened – 'Thank God,' said his mother quietly.

At the Balmore Drive Action Station, Ken and his men were sat around the wireless which one had acquired for the station. It worked with an accumulator for power but that was no problem. Those among the men who actually owned a set themselves were well used to regular trips to corner shops to get them recharged.

As fast as the part-timers arrived, summoned by the siren, Ken made up the crews and sent them off on the pre-determined routes. A heavy mist hung over the hills around the Thames Valley, and Caversham Heights was encompassed. With the All Clear, the men began arriving back wet through.

Ken cursed silently to himself. He was angry enough about the patrolling system, but more so that the Chief Fire Officer and councillors had decided that firemen did not need waterproofs.

First time out when at war and they were soaked, with no change of uniform for comfort as they remained on duty. 'All the patrolling is taking place in open lorries and even waterproof leggings are refused,' he ranted at John. His Number Two, realising that it was another outburst of commonsense, quietly said, 'Why?' 'Because someone says they will hamper a man climbing a ladder or an escape. Who ever heard of such nonsense!'

It wasn't long into the war before the order came to scrap the patrol system. 'Hurrah,' said Ken to John. 'The reason given is to save petrol. I agree with that, but it is also saving someone's reputation, I reckon.'

The controversy over leggings, which raised anger at stations all over the town, took much longer to resolve before Reading came into line with others.

Fires remained rare in the town and there was little for them to do as back up to the 'brass hats' – except race to get to a fire before the powerful big new Dennis pump-escape. A tall order as it was better placed in the new purpose-built civic fire station.

*   *   *

The delivery, in January 1939, of the powerful traditional red engine, ARD 780, capable of 80 mph, complete with modern wheeled 50-foot escape, was a tonic. An eight-tonner, the proud claim was that it could climb hills at 35 to 40 mph, which was no mean feat.

The opening just two months after war was declared of the large and effective fire station in Caversham Road, was a transformation of the town's fire-fighting capability. Built under the requirements of the all-changing Fire Brigades Act, the tender accepted in 1938 was £23,236 8s 5d.

Equally vital in the recognition of the fire service was the appointment of the Fire Chief as Chief Officer, no longer was he subservient to the Chief Constable, although he was 'officially' the administrator.

Gordon Castle was to remember his first ride on the new engine. 'It's a lovely machine,' he told Ken afterwards. 'The driver nearly tore the gearbox out, the gears are reverse to RD 111. It did 70 mph nearly flat out, and it has a windscreen.'

The station with its three double doors fronting a massive appliance room, had proper offices and workshops, with civilised rest room above. Behind was a large training yard and drill tower, and nine houses, so 'brass hats' could at last live on the spot, increasing the speed and numbers to fight a fire.

It could hardly be believed by the regulars and AFS who moved in. Such a contrast to the Butts. It was a great day for the firemen when they all marched behind the pristine fire engine to their new home. Cheers echoed from the people on the pavements as they saw how smart they were, though the gasmasks and steel helmets still chilled many who could remember 'The war to end wars!'

There were a few cheers, although not so loud, from the AFS left to themselves at The Butts as an action station. There was a bit more room and they could at least sort themselves out and turn it into somewhere to eat and sleep. What a headache for them, and all the other action stations, creating something from virtually nothing.

*　　　*　　　*

Yet, a year later, the new station was close to being wiped out! One of the first bombs to drop on the town landed 100 or so yards away – as the bomber flies – destroying two terraced houses in Cardiff Road. The reality was clear.

The 'brass hats' were in a dilemma. They were still the principal unit answering the normal fire calls. But, they could see the world was changing so fast. Their agreement, as in so many towns, said they were not to go out of the borough. In many town's they voiced their feelings of unfairness. But, it was not to change – yet.

*　　　*　　　*

Six action stations were chosen in the town and opened as war was declared. In addition to the old and new fire stations, Caversham and Oxford Road, there was the Hamilton Road garage, on the main road to Wokingham, and Gowrings Garage. Most travellers who drove through the town from London to the West knew it. It was in Pell Street, on the main route.

Some of the new pumps had been stored there since the crisis. When the AFS were called up, they moved in and took over part of Gowrings' premises.

Just as everywhere else, these men had to use their own initiative to make themselves comfortable. There was nowhere to sleep. First nights were uncomfortable on the floor! Scrounging was the only resort. Wood made bunks, chicken wire was stretched across and, miraculously, mattresses were obtained.

It was the same everywhere. In some places, even worse. At one station near Slough there was not even a way of boiling water! Those who owned vacuum flasks brought them full of hot water. The men were soon in hot water for another reason. People like Ken and Gordon laughed when they heard the story, because they could understand. One of the firemen was sent by an officer to the factory next door with metal strips, which he said he had 'fiddled' to make name plates.

'See if you can get these drilled.' The firemen asked, 'Can I see the works manager?' when he arrived. 'Yes, he could drill them,' was the reply, adding, 'but it is the first time anyone has pinched metal plates and then come back and asked me to drill them.'

At another in Berkshire, some material was delivered to use for blackout curtains. 'Scrim,' whispered three firemen, who had been window cleaners. In no time it was cut up into rolls and lost!

41

There was good fortune for men on duty at one of the Slough stations. Six recruits arrived just as the duty men were starting to dig a hole to house a double Anderson air raid shelter. A fire call took them from their task. The officer interviewing the six, asked, 'What are you trained at?' 'Navvies,' was the reply, 'We all come from one firm.'

'Come and see what the boys were doing,' he said. They looked at each other, 'Do you want this dug out?' asked one in an Irish brogue. 'Leave it to us.' In no time they were back in the station – 'It's ready.' They were very popular when the crew returned.

*   *   *

Ken was making sure there were no spare hours for the men to become bored. Much useful work was done in those early days of the war. Drilling and exercises continued into the night. 'I want these men to be as capable of finding a hydrant and getting to work by night as they are in the day,' Ken insisted to John. 'I know I am exposing them to risks of accidents, but the risks are going to be greater if they aren't expert when it really starts.'

The first month or so was a nerve racking period for these men. Pumps and equipment were standing out in the open. 'Do you realise, we are standing by like this in our thousands all over the country, waiting for the blow to fall – Where? – When?' said Ken to John. 'Yes, and we're groaning about squeezing a quart into a pint pot,' with everybody in this hut.'

In December, John's worry was answered. The Corporation notified Ken that the Action Station was to be moved to another part of the district, to the remains of a famous old house, Caversham Court, with its grounds running down to the River Thames. Returning from a recce, Ken said, 'It sounds fabulous, but it's in a terrible state.' Really, he had a pretty good idea what to expect as it was only a couple of hundred yards from his home and hairdresser's shop. At least that was useful.

What was left of demolished Caversham Court were disused coach houses in a courtyard, with garages adjoining. These were welcome to Ken to provide somewhere to house his pumps and vehicles. Arrangements began immediately to move men and equipment. 'Unit by unit,' he said,'so that we remain ready for action.'

A telephone was installed, but no heating or lighting was laid on until the men had been there two or three days. It was the start of a bitter winter, and the place had not been used for years, 'I doubt if a mortuary could be colder,' said Ken.

Men used to working outdoors in bad weather sat at night, wrapped in blankets, with their lips blue with cold, as they huddled around a hurricane lamp. Sleep was impossible.

'Do you realise, we are supposed to be fairly lucky? I heard today that there are men sleeping under railway arches in other parts of the country. The luckiest are said to be those sleeping in condemned schools!'

'It's all the fault of local authorities, who haven't prepared,' he added tersely.

There were no cleansing or drying facilities. Pigeon droppings, where they had been coming through the roof, were everywhere. The men decided to sort things

42

out for themselves, as there was no help coming. The lavatory would not work, it was blocked. Ken borrowed a set of rods, they opened the manholes and cleared the drains themselves.

The tradesmen in the crews, soon scrounged a tortoise stove and got some heating going. But it was only when Ken said, 'If we don't soon receive some coke my men are going to start cutting down the trees,' that it arrived. Others acquired old car seats which they turned into armchairs. Quickly, by themselves, they made the rooms above the garages as snug as possible. The two low beams in the rest room, just 5 ft 6 in from the floor, looked attractive, but concentrated the minds when men dashed for the stairs as the bells went down!

The men became quite adept at this and then, Alec Hunt forgot and split his head open on the beam. That was enough for Ken. The carpenters among the men cut a hole through the floor and scrounging a scaffolding pole, smoothed it down, produced and fitted a workmanlike copy of a real firemen's pole. Sliding down that was a quick way to the vehicles below, and it avoided the beams. 'It seems action is better than asking for instructions,' said Ken, and he remembered that for the rest of the war.

*   *   *

Moving into Caversham Court was a strange experience for Ken. Artifacts from the original house were still stored in the coach house. A panelled gateway, a staircase, stained glass windows, half an orange ceiling, with gold leaf, blue background, and cherubs, cut into quarters. Ken remembered that well, it took eight men to lift each section. Under the eye of the Chief Fire Officer it was taken carefully on lorries and stored in Emmer Green. Carefully the men stacked it under instruction. He could not realise that after the war he would find boilers, to be used in case of a blitz, chests of tea and food, had been dumped on top of the treasures!

7 · Phoney war

As the first nerve-wracking weeks gave way to months of a phoney war, some men, in common with a large part of Britain's population, began to think that stalemate had been reached. It seemed like a giant chess match with the armies facing each other, and no game being played.

Ken Watson realised what was going on. 'These men reason that there will be no action by the German Air Force, but more important that their time is being wasted. They say their services would be better in industry.' He added, looking up at John Lander, 'Where they would be getting real wages.

'Who can blame them. with a fireman's wage of £2 18s 6d a week.'

John knew that deep down Ken did not entirely support them but, he was bitter, as were the men, at the public's attitude to Civil Defence, and especially against firemen.

'Look at the London Press story, 'London firemen to be sacked'.' Ken realised the men in the provinces could see this spreading to them, 'But nobody's been sacked. My guess is that someone wants to give the idea that fire service expenditure is being cut.'

John responded, 'Did you read somewhere a town councillor said 'frankly he did not know why firemen wanted overcoats'. If we get a blitz, perhaps he would like to ride on top of a lorry in this winter.'

There were other worries for Ken, on the last day of the year it was announced that all men from 20 to 28 were to be called up. That was soon to make some gaps in the AFS ranks. It was the dilly-dallying by the authorities that again was angering him. 'When these men signed on as volunteers, we were all under the impression that the age limit was 25 to 50. That was what the forms stated.

'Now the war has started we're informed that it's gone up to 30! The men of 25 are some of the finest chaps we have, full of enthusiasm, keen and quick. I bet they will be back when the blitz starts, because it will.'

For many of those called-up their training and experience was not wasted, they found their way into the Army Fire Service.

At the same time, nationally the Fire Brigades Union was also showing its teeth. As a result chief officers were granted a series of deferments by the Home Office, but not before many of the best men had gone.

'Today, the AFS changes,' went on Ken. 'Many of the men who are conscripted to join us to make up the loss will be OK, but the others are not going to be happy about it.' 'Wait and see,' said John, 'but I reckon you're right. Everything we have achieved has been against the odds simply because of their enthusiasm as volunteers.'

The sirens sounded just at that minute, just like a baleful, mocking laugh. They kept sounding at varying intervals but nothing happened. Everybody was beginning to get decidedly browned off.

Ken watched as everyone grabbed their gear from the vehicles. Boots, axes on their belts, steel helmets and gasmasks, were positioned ever ready for the bells to go down, for men to climb on or jump into the lorries and cars dressing as best they could, as fast as they could. Once again they were off to their action points at Holloways Garage, the Black Horse, Emmer Green, Richmond Road, and Shepherd's Lane.

He listened quietly; there was a curse as the strap of one man's respirator case twisted behind his back, and a friend had to sort it out for him to thread the cord and lash it tight to the case. Several voices were raised as one of the old crash-gearbox taxis refused to start. It was as though the former town-centre workhorse was feeling as belligerent as the men.

All Ken's men were as convinced, as thousands of others across the country had been led to believe, that as soon as war started so would the bombing. Now, in the stark cold of that first winter of disbelief, with sirens interrupting lives, and especially sleep, still nothing massive had happened.

The curses, he realised, veiled the questions: Had they been misled? Had so much of their time been wasted? He knew it was only the diligent carrying out of exercises, not only at their own station but between the various districts, that was keeping the men together. It wasn't the best moment to be thinking of unwilling conscripts, he hoped that John's optimism would prove right.

Then he remembered all those innocents in Spain, killed by German bombers. By God, he was going to be ready – and so were his men. Any conscripts were going to have to get the volunteer spirit!

Helping keep the spirits up were the visits to the new Central Fire Station. This looked really imposing, with its big double-doors out of which fire engines could dash without any of the previous backing and filling. A control room ran down one side and, up above, there were real living quarters!

What a change, and what a tonic. Even the AFS men who had taken over the old building in the Butts were giving the place a sense of 'home', now that men were living there all the time.

The visits to the new fire station were to receive instruction on the new equipment and appliances being issued by the Home Office. 'This morning,' said Ken, as his men fell in on parade, 'we are going again to the central station. I think you will find this training interesting.' One or two eyebrows lifted, they wondered what was coming next. 'Sheet jumping,' he added in his dry away.

When they arrived the reality needed little explanation, a huge sheet was spread out and men told off to hold tight to the edges. 'Your bodies must be braced to withstand the shock of a man, or woman, landing in the sheet.' The others were ordered to climb the stairs inside the drill tower, to be rescued.

Perched on the edge of the hard concrete window cill, the instructor said loudly,

'Always remember, you must step off the cill, do not attempt to jump!' Not easy, when looking down from that height. 'It looks like a bloody pocket handkerchief,' quipped the first man. Then he was gone – safely.

The exercise was successfully completed. As the men returned to the Caversham fire station, the instructor's words were still ringing in their ears, 'These sheets are only used as a last resort, as a means of life saving!'

Alec Hunt was laughing. 'Just think, I didn't intend to join the AFS. I was employed by a public works' contractor, and I saw all the posters, 'Join the ARP', 'Join the AFS', 'Men wanted for the Rescue', and decided I would be best in the Rescue. But they wouldn't have me, the boss man was from Collier and Catley and he had enough of his own men. So I went next door and joined the AFS. Now I'm jumping out of the sky! I must be mad.'

Ken was quietly chuckling. At least he was always prepared to have a go at anything his men were asked to do and this had proved highly stimulating. 'It certainly helped to break the monotony,' he told John afterwards.

A university type on the station helped ease the monotony of the food. Rabbits ran around in The Warren grounds, 'Can I shoot them?' he asked Ken. He sat on the steps and potted a special treat for lunch. That got the rest into action again, they obtained and fitted a coke stove to do the cooking! Some proved to be good cooks.

*   *   *

Ordinary fire calls were now regularly answered by the AFS men. With the poor quality dusty coal which was often the best 'ration' that householders could obtain, and the need to keep the blackout complete, chimney fires were one of the biggest problems, as well as dirtiest.

But certainly not the most dangerous! Caversham Mill, not far from the station, was one factory which would always be exercising Ken Watson's mind. Far removed from its original peaceful purpose, driven by the waters of the River Thames, it was now a factory producing magnesium and aluminium powder, for bombs.

Three or four times in those early days of the war fire broke out. Central fire station always received the call direct and then notified the Caversham AFS. The importance of answering such a call was readily recognised and Ken made sure his men kept on their toes. Great was his joy the night his crew turned out so smartly that they beat the central station men to the factory.

The rest of his senses were more subdued, the glare of the fire could be seen for many miles. 'I hope the RAF have some fighter cover, or we could attract a lot of nasty attention,' said Ken.

'This factory should give us all the experience we need to learn how best to fight incendiary bombs,' Ken told his men after the first couple of blazes. With uniforms silver-plated from top to bottom, their minds were thinking of getting clean, rather than waging a war.

'I have a theory that the training we have been given of spraying water on the bombs is wrong.' He went on to elaborate that he believed if water was applied to electron metal in large quantities, and not sprayed, the water would separate itself into hydrogen and oxygen.

The men were used to Ken fighting his way through the science of fire-fighting, often against the 'experts', and they listened carefully. 'If extra oxygen accelerates the combustion, it increases tenfold the fire. Then the material or metal will often explode, and scatter burning fragments over a fair distance. These can then be easily dealt with.

'It will only work on small fires, like incendiary bombs!' he added clearly. 'When next you find these bombs being slung at you, do not spray as we have been taught, I want you to use the jet.' He was right, and when the civilian street Fire Guards were formed, Ken and others taught them to use the jet of the stirrup pump.

Back at the factory, inside the building their method of extinguishing the burning heaps of electron powder was to cover them with special sand. It prevented the spread of the trouble: outside water was used. All Reading's firemen had a good grounding in the peculiarities of the inflammable metal which the German bombers rained down, and so nearly brought Britain to its knees.

*   *   *

Meanwhile, firemen from the Gowrings station were in real trouble. Answering a call to a chimney fire at night, they climbed on the roof with a stirrup pump but to no avail. 'Fetch up a length of hose,' and they did. Pointing the branch nozzle down the chimney, and turning on the standpipe, the water deluged into the house.

It was a mess. Out in the yard were some ducks. 'It made a good pond for them,' said one as the story was retold. The adrenalin might run fast with an alert on but, clearly, devilment was going to be paid for.

Fortunately, the landlord of the local, the Turks Head, saved them. He vouched that there was a light showing from the fire and, with the siren sounded, the firemen had done right in putting it out quickly.

*   *   *

White as a sheet, the AFS man came back into the cosy warm room which his crew were lucky enough to be able to use as an action point. Cups of tea were brought to the crews by the nurses, they were well looked after at the Royal Berkshire Hospital.

The siren had gone yet again that night, eight warnings in all! Bored with it all, the fireman wandered off. Tonight, a door that was always locked, was not. He walked through – and came back with a shattered, colourless look on his face. 'What's the matter?' asked his leading fireman. 'You come and look in here.' They all did – it was the mortuary. He had opened one of the drawers!

*   *   *

There was a shock, too, for a new AFS man at the central station. Despite his thick glasses he was still welcome as a volunteer. Fetching the tray of cocoa one night, he walked through the wrong doors – and fell helplessly down the hole of the pole shaft.

*   *   *

Although the Home Office could not do more than persuade civic leaders what they should be doing, the Government's 'regional man', H M Smith, started to appear regularly. His post seemed the only liaison between fire brigades. 'He's trying to put some sense into it all,' Gordon Castle told Ken Watson.

They were comparing notes after he had spent an April day watching them drill with pumps on Thames-side. Just days earlier 'brass hats' and AFS had worked together in Station Square, very publicly outside the important railway stations. The following Sunday the AFS were back in the square with a full-blooded practice of what might happen; the next evening, they were exercising with the Air Raid Wardens.

Then, 13 days later the Government's muscle-man was back visiting all the AFS stations. That was a fillip for all the auxiliaries. Sirens were being tested, gas lectures and tests were going ahead at the Silver Street 'chamber', the deteriorating situation, and then Dunkirk, had everyone jumping.

H M's Inspector made a surprise call on Gordon Castle.

'He came into Wokingham Road station and turned us out,' started Gordon's story to Ken. 'Fire at the old cottages at Manor Farm,' was the message.

The cottages were burning well, when the AFS men got there. 'This is no theory,' said Gordon, as he looked at the barbed wire, a wall and other debris, between him and the fire. 'Come on men, we can do it.' Under and over the wire and rubbish, they crawled their way in, making a path for their pump which they dragged through behind them.

Gordon demanded they took the pump because he was sure in his own mind that there was a stream nearby, which led into the River Kennet. He was right and the firemen quickly got to work and put the blaze out. Mr Smith was pleased at the positive action. 'You did a damned good job,' he told the men.

*   *   *

There was action for Ken's men in similar exercises. He was very conscious of the problem of communication with the central station if the two Thames' bridges were destroyed. 'Very likely, and obvious targets,' was his comment to John as they discussed plans. 'We must exercise in Caversham as if we are on our own.'

They were hard at work, near to the two cinemas, one evening, part-timers as well as full-time AFS, on a tough exercise. 'Messenger,' shouted Ken, and the boy came running. 'Get this message to Caversham Road fire station.' 'Yes, sir.' 'But,' said Ken holding him back, 'both Caversham and Reading bridges are down.'

Off he went; half an hour later he was back. 'I've done that, sir,' he said. 'How the hell did you get there?' There was a smile on the messenger's face, 'Over the

48

Clappers, the footplank over the river weir, and then over the lock gates.' Ken allowed himself a smile as well. 'Good, you know your patch.'

But Reading's Chief Officer was also well aware of the important riverside works of Thorneycroft and Elliotts, engineers and woodworkers. Huge exercises across Caversham tested all the action stations. Also special attention had to be given to the Government's 'secret' wireless centre at Caversham Park.

Water supplies always concerned Ken, despite the Thames being so near. 'Buckside, it's our obvious spot to pump water, we can get the pump to it so easily from the station,' was the start of another move to ensure they were prepared. 'If we dig a big hole, a cistern, we can beat the shallows.' Off went Ken to the Thames Conservancy yard to borrow some thigh boots.

Sinking the hole in the water took a long time. Every shovelful of mud felt like a ball and chain as it oozed water when dug out. When it was finished, Ken took the boots back. 'What did you want them for?' casually asked the Thames-wise man. 'We have been digging a big cistern, to act as a static water supply in case of bombing,' he said proudly.

With a laugh, the devastating reply came. 'You've been wasting your time, it will be full of sand in two days, it's a backwash!' He was right, just a day later, Ken found it almost full.

Not to be deterred, Ken told John, 'It must be possible to pump water from our own Caversham Court grounds, even if we cannot get the pump near the depth of water we need.' A regular firemen, looking on, said, 'No.' 'We will have a go, and show we can provide water right into the centre of Caversham,' responded Ken.

That concentrated John's thinking. It needed to be, because on the Sunday morning, the Chief Officer was watching. With all the men available, Ken ordered the suction hose to be taken from all the pumps and carried down to the river bank. Just one major Coventry Climax pump was manhandled there as well.

His action then was contrary to all rule books, Ken ordered sections of the heavy armoured suction hose to be coupled up. These were pushed out into the river, a third added. Then a fourth, fifth, sixth, and so on. There was no way water could be lifted that far in normal routine and some heads were shaking. But, Ken was banking on the fact that because the pump was only six feet above the river-bed strainer, the water would reach the pump. He was right. From there it was passed to one of the light Worthington Simpson pumps at the road entrance and then on into the shopping centre, where a jet sprayed vigorously.

Buoyed by his success, Ken arranged another exercise on the Thames-side Promenade. He took all five of his light pumps and set up a relay alongside the river, with firemen handling two jets at the far end of the crocodile of hose and pumps.

Going to the second pump, he ordered 'Knock off your pump, couple up the hose.' With the pump 'out of action' the water continued to flow. Walking to Number four pump, he repeated his instruction. Still the water flowed. Theoretically it should have failed to reach the jets.

There were some amazed looks, although his own men were well used to his educated approach to fire fighting. Ken then cut out one of the jets and gave the

49

same orders to Number three pump. There were cheers as water still came from the jet. The Caversham men were just as pleased as Ken himself – they really felt they could look after their own patch if the bridges were down.

But, 'What if the bridges were still intact?' And, 'What a test to see if we can lift water that high?' No sooner had the thoughts run through Ken's head than he decided to have a try. Off to elegant Caversham Bridge, a main artery across the mighty Thames, with a heavy pump.

They manoeuvred it across the flagstone pavement into one of the redoubts and got busy. The message reached the council officers and the Chief arrived, cursing them because it was thought the pump was likely to go through the bridge's paving stones!

Ken laughed, he did not really care, 'We've got a lift,' he shouted with delight. Seconds later, there was a cry as an old lady fell into the water and the firemen ran and rescued her. The council crisis was forgotten.

8 · White feathers

Ken Watson was always up early and first to collect the post. It had been a short night, he had been late at the action station working as ever. Today he could manage a few hours helping his father in the shop.

But when he opened a handwritten envelope he exploded. Inside was yet another white feather! The quill was pushed through a plain piece of nondescript paper. There was no written message – it was left to make its own suggestion. The writing on the envelope was different again to the others. It looked like a woman's, although made childlike to disguise.

'Some chattering stupid woman, upset because her husband was called up into the Army, thinks I should be there as well. That's my guess,' he said to Lucy who had come rushing when she heard him shout. 'And I am not the only fireman to get them.'

He was seething, 'I have spent a whole lot of our time, as a volunteer, getting ready for war, and she, and the others, can't see it coming – to them,' he added carefully. 'If Hitler hits us like his planes did Spain, then they'll squeal.'

*   *   *

Suddenly the war started in earnest. In eleven days, in May 1940, the German Panzers had swept round the flank of the Maginot Line to the sea. Operation Dynamo began to evacuate troops from Dunkirk.

It was clear that Britain was in great danger. Ken tried desperately to throw aside his anger that he, and other hard-working AFS volunteers, who had been giving up their own time since 1938, should be treated as cowards. It was a repeat of the wicked tactics of some during the first World War.

The national appeal for people to form a civilians' army, the Local Defence Volunteers, was going to hurt recruitment to the AFS. Under strength as the fire service was, clearly it was going to have a tough time, as he had said so often. 'Thank God, those who stayed on during the phoney war are a great lot of chaps,' he told Lucy. 'The silly bitches sending those feathers are in for a shock themselves if Hitler does invade us.'

Within days the survivors started to be landed, shattered and very many without guns. Sent home for a brief respite, everybody could see what airborne war was all about.

'What about the Massey Shaw at Dunkirk?' Tom Goldsmid, again was first with the story to tell his Caversham colleagues. Firemen were proud to learn of the exploits of the London Fire Brigade's 78-foot fire boat, named after their famous chief officer.

It was the first time the Massey Shaw had sailed outside her famous river – since delivery from Cowes five years earlier – but, when the call came for little ships to cross the Channel, to lift men off the beaches, she went.

'Three times she crossed the Channel,' said Tom, excitedly. 'With her broad beam, she packed the troops aboard like sardines and so rescued hundreds. Bombs and machine gun bullets were all around her.

'There was a problem when they wanted 12 volunteers for a crew. The whole of the river service, nearly 400 men, wanted to go. They picked six regulars and six AFS. An ex-Lowestoft fisherman, Station Officer Youngman was in charge.'

He was proud as a Londoner, despite what Hitler thought of Jews, and hastily added, 'I bet you didn't know an auxiliary fireman was left on the harbour jetty when she made a quick exit on the last trip? He got back on another troop carrier.'

Belgium gave in; Mussolini declared war on Britain; and then, the fall of France. Ken was almost demonic as he read the newspapers and listened to the wireless. Bad as it all sounded, he realised it was probably worse with the censors controlling what was printed or broadcast.

He was stirred by Churchill's fighting speech, by his demand that the Local Defence Volunteers be given a real name, Home Guard. That's what they would have to be.

Whatever happened, Ken knew the AFS would not give up without a fight – and he felt sure they were going to have one.

*   *   *

Men might be what the LDV was calling for but, Margaret Belman, knew she must do something too. A typist in an office not far from the central fire station, she quickly made up her mind. Returning from her lunch break, she said to her friend, 'I am going to join the AFS. They need women to be telephonists, to take over men's work in the control room.' She nodded in its direction.

Margaret clearly meant it. 'If you're going, I am coming too,' said her friend. Off they went to breach the male-only bastion. Things may have looked black for the country but it was all still very British: off to the town hall, forms to fill, interview and medical.

Steel helmet and service gasmask; No uniform, 'Please wear trousers'; No nights! Seven am to 2 pm and 2 pm to 10 pm – and the men had only to look in the direction of the tiny office and they were in trouble! Still there were plenty of air raid warnings during those hours to keep the girls busy and in touch with the other stations.

'Just think,' said Margaret to her friend, 'if we had worn trousers to work before the war!' 'You would never have had to go through a gas chamber then, either,' her friend replied.

*   *   *

52

At the Oxford Road station, the pattern of preparation was the same. Gas and smoke drills, first aid, chair knot practice from the upstairs window, pumping relays from the Thames, and, it seemed every morning, gas mask inspection. 'Action bell, practice turn out – 27 seconds,' Roger Smith wrote in the report book, as the crews dashed to yet another imaginary bomb incident.

He was remembering the atmosphere on the Sunday, just two days after the dramatic appeal for people to join the LDV – when the AFS were asked for volunteers to stop parachutists. As soon as the crews switched their day and night shifts at 1 pm, the immediate order was, 'Clean and examine all gas clothing.'

Then a few days later, all full and part-timers went to the Silver Street gas chamber. There, instructors used tear gas capsules to create the atmosphere; proving the gasmasks did not leak by making everyone go through twice, the second time without wearing one.

Now, another 28 sets of anti-gas clothing had been delivered. Also another Worthington Simpson pump. The huge national delivery was now complete.

As he looked back at the report book, he did not need to look at the date. He was going to remember it for a long time: June 1st, Mobilisation Day. All full-time AFS were now signed on for the duration.

There was greater excitement among the men when a frying pan and an electric hotplate arrived.

The stirrup pump instruction was also bringing out the crowds, 400 at Norcot School – most people were getting the message.

Sometimes when they should not! Roger chuckled, but the chiefs did not, when a warden repeated fire calls, to the central fire station. They were part of an exercise for their own Tilehurst and West Reading district. The red machines came with bells clanging, thinking 'Fire at Battle School' was for real.

Sometimes there were real fires they could all join in, a Services' Club in London Street burnt out, damage at the vital Thorneycroft engineering factory, and the Army's Ranikhet Camp in Tilehurst. Plus, training Brock Barracks soldiers to defend themselves from fire.

*   *   *

Ken was writing up his diary. June 25 – 'Times have changed. Twice the sirens have sounded. We are on our own.' As the All Clear started, he completed his entry '1.7 am to 3.23 am, and 11.16 pm to 3.17 am. That's a long day!' Long exasperating days were to follow.

*   *   *

High summer seemed like High Noon for the firemen. In the August sunshine, the Luftwaffe began intensive raids on RAF airfields. Brize Norton was one that was hit and 46 planes were destroyed. At Croydon where a large formation thought to be 'ours' caused death and destruction, firemen turned their hoses on frantic people to calm them. Nearer home Wallingford's LDV were reporting a plane down over Moreton.

53

Five warnings another night, it grew to eight; an exercise cancelled because of warnings, then a huge common fire raging at Bucklebury, with the fear of enemy planes attacking. A few nights later, a minute after a purple warning ended, a hayrick and lorries went up at a Tilehurst farm. Ordinary fires were now a danger with a new meaning, but soon such problems were suddenly to seem inconsequential.

Still the 'Alerts' seemed to be coming and going the whole time. One special telephone warning to Ken was stark: it was clear that Hitler was going all out to defeat the British air force. 'That means he really is intent on invasion,' he told John Lander. 'It's the 13th, I shall remember this August – at least I hope I will.' Firemen were told to look out for parachutists – the codeword for an attack was 'Cromwell'.

Men at Gordon Castle's station were more affected by the aerodrome bombings, and really keyed-up. They were nearest to Woodley Aerodrome, where aircraft technicians were working flat-out building new planes – and the initial pilot training was vital. As if telepathic, hit-and-run raiders started dropping bombs there.

All remembered the story in the Berkshire Chronicle, in June 1938, that Phillips and Powis had been given the biggest contract for building new aeroplanes ever placed with a firm in Britain. The Air Ministry had chosen the Miles Kestrel monoplane as the latest training machine. Even then it would not say how many, but the rival Reading Standard's report said, 'it was several times greater than the 200 machines ordered from America'.

The Kestrel was in addition to the Miles Magisters they were already building, 'for initial training of service pilots'.

Tom Goldsmid, who had moved to Caversham to start his own business some time before the war, was showing an incredible knack of knowing what was going on in London. True it was rumour, but so often he had the guts of the truth, and his mates listened.

He arrived with bad news. He had earlier told Ken that London firemen were helping men drawn from all over the Cambridge region trying to cope with an incredibly fierce fire sweeping six bombed tanks of an oil installation at Thameshaven, on the East Coast. It was going to burn for more than a fortnight, was his latest.

But this time, via London, his news was of a similar oil fire at Pembroke Docks, in Wales. 'Five firemen have perished,' he said. 'There was a great gush of burning oil and they were trapped. The Jerries have been making repeated air attacks as the men fight the fires.'

'We are in it for real,' said Ken quietly.

*   *   *

Every time the sirens sounded AFS and messengers came rushing from their homes. Within two minutes the first pumps would be on their way to action points, so would the first from the back-of-the-pub sub-station. As men and lorries arrived the equipment would be thrown on board, pumps hitched on, and away. Nine pumps from just that one station. It soon became well rehearsed.

Then, when the All Clear sounded they would return, unload the lorries, and start for home – they probably wouldn't get very far ... It was being repeated at all six stations in Reading, and their sub-stations. Also by AFS with the volunteer brigades around, and all over huge areas of the country.

There was a special chill with messages that continued to come. 'Gas goggles and 13 tins of anti-gas ointment to be collected from the central fire station'. 'Who's superstitious?' grunted Roger. But, especially those it relayed to the Home Guard: 'Please collect 12 rifles as soon as possible', 'Two Browning automatics are available', 'You can have 36 Mills bombs, instruction to begin at once'. At last something with which to fight back.

Then, to cap everything, a message that overcoats for the civvy army had arrived. The firemen were still waiting!

One had to read in the significance as the Home Guard were told 'Sunday's church parade is cancelled', and the Chief Fire Officer, for the first time, telephoned, 'Number 1 regional crew to stand-by with a heavy pump in case needed for distant calls!

'I remember that Saturday night,' Roger told Harold Randle. 'It was 7.15 pm. A little later he rang again, and said 'Collect iron rations from the central station before leaving the borough'. It was nearly two hours – a long two hours – before he said 'Stand down'. Within ten minutes there was another purple warning.'

Many airfields and towns became targets as the Luftwaffe pressed home their attacks. 'Six large raids during the day,' Ken wrote in his diary. He did not know then of the devastation that was to follow as 500 planes turned on Portsmouth and Southampton and their vital docks and ships.

Reading area was just one of many places to receive some attention during the night. But while they were doing their best at home, Portsmouth was suffering the worst – 117 were dead and 99 seriously injured.

The whole of England and Wales, south of the Humber, was repeatedly under red or purple alerts.

The day after the Portsmouth onslaught the RAF made its first raid on Berlin. 'That really is going to upset the dictator.' He was right.

9 · Luftwaffe strikes!

September, 1940, the Luftwaffe struck! Suddenly the routine daily log books in many fire stations like Ken Watson's, across the country, were recording history. It was the time for which auxiliaries had worked and waited.

During August firemen had been busy with the wreckage from the Battle of Britain and the first real raids. Suddenly the public seemed to realise the threatening menace and that firemen were not dodging the column, but in the front of the frontline.

People living around the fighter aerodromes, and the factories frantically building new planes to combat the losses in the battle, learnt in the weeks before that it was as dreadful as all the pleas for ARP volunteers, and AFS firemen in particular, had spelt out.

'It's a long time since those first bombs on the Orkneys in October 1939.' Ken and John Lander were taking time to ensure that everything possible was ready, as the bombings started. 'This is nothing yet, I am sure,' went on Ken. 'All those buzzes about reconnaissance flights as far as Bristol and Merseyside, they could soon mean plenty of action. Make sure we are ready.'

It was a usual routine day on Saturday, September 7. But at teatime that was to change for ever, when the sky above London filled with bombers and fighters. 'Central control room received a message that there were nearly 400,' Ken told his men. The stories going round were graphic.

Tom Goldsmid looked drained as he came rushing into their tiny mess room. 'They have dropped bombs on Woolwich Arsenal, Millwall docks, Limehouse, Rotherhithe, Tower Bridge, Surrey Docks, and West Ham power station!' He sounded like a railway announcer as he rattled off all the well-known names. 'And they were gone again within an hour,' he added.

How he found out, how much was correct did not really matter, to them it was clear that the phoney war was over for ever.

A fresh wave of raiders came in again just after 8 pm: it was easy, they were guided by the glare from the fires the previous onslaught had started. High explosives and incendiaries hurtled down, increasing the damage and destruction below. Later, when there was time, word spread through the fire brigades' grapevine that the fire area was four miles long and one mile wide, plus all the smaller fires scattered around. Pathetic victims were everywhere, dead and dying. When there was time to count, the register was 430 civilians killed and 1,600 seriously injured.

The telephone rang in the Caversham action station at 9 pm, as it was doing in many other stations in a vast ring around the capital. A regional call had gone out for reinforcements. The message was simple, official orders were to send a crew to report to West Drayton fire station, to muster to go into London.

There was no hesitation, or even time for Ken to rush along the road to tell his wife, Lucy. A part-timer had already reported for his night duty and he promptly volunteered to make up the crew. A messenger raced off to round up others at their homes, full-time men who were off duty, ordering them to report back and cover the fire station, another man was dialling the few who were in contact by phone.

The engine on the Packard was running, the pump was hitched on behind, and away. Everyone's adrenalin was running even faster than normal. As the car swung on to the main road, auxiliaries were already running to respond. Ken saw a full-timer, Joe, shouting at him to stop, but he was stopping for no-one.

Each of the town's action stations were sending a crew and Ken was worried as he arrived at the pre-arranged meeting place, so they could travel together. There was nobody there! 'We must be behind them coming from Caversham,' he said. 'Step on it,' he told the driver. And they did.

Reaching the main line railway bridge, on the edge of town, the Home Guard volunteers, were on guard and alert with their guns. They could see the glow in the sky, and knew something grim was up.

Ken stopped, it was wise anyhow. 'Has a convoy of fire pumps passed through?' 'No,' was the answer. 'Roy, go back to that telephone kiosk, it's only 50 yards, and ring the central station, tell them we are at the bridge and waiting for the others,' he ordered.

Just as the man was on the telephone, the others arrived. Hanging on to the side of one was Joe, the very man who had been shouting to his mates to stop for him! Joe had cycled like blazes to the central fire station, dropped his bicycle, and jumped on the pump as it drove out.

Immediately the convoy moved off. Ken assumed that Roy, talking on the telephone would return to the Caversham station. As Roy came out of the kiosk, he could see the rear lights of his pump disappearing along the road. There was no way he was going to be left out of the excitement. He stopped the first vehicle coming along the road and demanded a lift all the way to the London docks. He finished up fire fighting at Wapping Steps and, when dawn broke, Roy, and the firemen he was with found the barge they were trying to save was loaded with mines!

Meanwhile, Ken's little convoy was joined by others as they made their way along the main London Road. 'They seem to be coming from all directions,' he grunted to his driver. The grunt was not because he was bad tempered but realising that something big was afoot. Never in his experience of exercises had they been mobilised like this. All the time up ahead, in the sky, was a glow which looked like an inverted saucer, with occasional twinkles like stars high above.

As they approached West Drayton, Ken could see London Transport buses parked along the sides of the road, the drivers and conductors standing in groups beside their blacked-out vehicles. All their eyes were watching the ever-brightening glow.

Presenting themselves at the West Drayton fire station, Ken found the streets packed with appliances and, inside, hundreds of other firemen who had been drawn from many miles around. Convoys were being formed. Just time for a quick cup of tea and a sandwich and Ken's crew found themselves already marshalled into a convoy too.

Just at that moment there was, what Ken later described to others back home, 'a hell of a crash!' Anti-aircraft guns opened up just away to their right. The whine of the shells and then their explosion far overhead. It was followed by the tinkle of falling shrapnel, as it bounced off the corrugated iron roof of the hut next to Ken.

'We all took good care to keep our heads down after that,' he recounted.

The order came to move. Ken's convoy swung back on to the London road and headed for Whitechapel fire station. 'Switch off your headlights,' said Ken. By now the glow in the sky was bright enough to do without them and, guided by the rear light of the pump in front, they all went hell-for-leather down the road. Accidents were miraculously avoided by the skilful handling of the over-weight vehicles.

Coming from London was a continuous stream of cars, large and small, crowded with people, bedding tied on the roofs of many, all, seemingly, obsessed with one idea, they wanted to get away from London as fast as they could.

'It's as if the city is doomed,' said Ken. 'They will be in their bloody panic,' said his driver. It was a mad flight, with cars crossing on to the convoy's side of the road, trying to pass all the other cars in their mad, panic-stricken haste.

Heaps of times the firemen drivers narrowly escaped hitting these cars head on – all simply ignoring the illuminated fire signs.

As they swept through the West End, the drivers turned off their sidelights, 'I could read a newspaper, if there was time,' said Ken. An earthly red glow seemed to pervade everywhere. On through Holborn, and down Cheapside, Ken expected to see the fire any minute.

On again, and still on, past The Bank, until they reached Bishopsgate. Just ahead Ken saw what appeared to be a huge timber yard ablaze from end to end. Firemen and lines of hose were everywhere.

'Christ,' uttered Ken, as he realised that, although this fire gave off a great deal of light, it was not the cause of the glow in the sky. 'The real fires are still ahead!' They pressed on.

Further on, by Gt. Eastern Street, fires were raging; turntable ladders were in action, hoses were like a spider's web across the road, other appliances were tearing about with bells clanging. it was an unforgettable sight.

Ken's convoy pressed on, passing fires to right and left, until it reached Whitechapel. He realised that was the right decision, big as they were those fires had in no way contributed a fraction to the main glare – 'which we have yet to encounter,' he added out loud. 'What?' said the driver. 'Sorry, nothing,' replied Ken. There was no point in adding to anybody's worries.

Armed sentries were guarding the entrance to the fire station as Ken, went in and reported. Men with rifles? Such a situation seemed beyond the imagination. One of the officers there said,'A lot of top people are expecting Hitler's invasion amid this confusion!' There was no time to worry, Ken was ordered to join a convoy just leaving and 'Report to the East India Dock gates.'

Outside again, Ken had difficulty in finding his own men and appliance, others were in the same state. Dozens more had arrived in their few brief minutes inside, and still more were arriving. It took time to extricate themselves from the traffic block but they managed it and, at last, were en route for the docks, and the 'glow'.

Passing the London Hospital there was a direct hit on the building ahead of Ken. Bricks showered down on convoy vehicles, and the road. 'If we had been three or four seconds earlier, we would have had it,' said Ken to the crew. 'That traffic shemozzle saved our lives.' For the men in the back, it was even more unnerving, sat uncomfortably on top of rolls of hose, and many sharp edges of other equipment.

A sudden flare ahead and a gas main fractured by explosives, burst into flames. There was no stopping them now. Over the fire they drove, and on. All were filled with a mad excitement that, at last, they were going to something big. The noise of the anti-aircraft guns and, even more, that strange tinkle of metal as the shrapnel fell back to earth, seemed as unbelievable as the bombs. Yet, it was heartening that someone was hitting back.

They reached within half-a-mile of the dock gates. Stop, came the signal. 'Unhitch the pumps and go on in the vehicles only.' Another quarter of a mile, then the order was, 'Park the vehicles in the side roads, go on on foot.' Over the debris littered streets they made their way to the docks. Here the sight for which they had all prepared themselves met their eyes.

There was a sharp intake of breath from Ken. Ahead, and away as far as he could see, there was one great sea of flames, with tottering walls every now and then crashing into the flames. 'What a smell!' Tea, flour, coffee, rubber, cigars, wood, all that the warehouses contained, were combining their peculiar odours into one overpowering smell.

*   *   *

It was a similar for Gordon Castle and his crew of five AFS men. They were making it as fast as their taxi could struggle, overloaded and tugging its heavy pump. Other such pumps were following Ken and Gordon, hot foot to London. Seven from the Reading area. Roger Smith's, from Tilehurst, had teamed up with the crew from Central, and he could see the 'Southern boys' from Gowrings just ahead. Who else? He did not know, and it did not matter. Much more important was that glow lighting up the sky – which the worried wives of all the Berkshire men could also see back home.

The Sonning Volunteer Brigade created a minor stir as they arrived in their streamlined all-enclosed engine. Designed by the father and son Edwards' team it was acclaimed as revolutionising fire engines when it was put into service in April 1938. Chief of the brigade was A F Edwards, but it was son Tom who was leading the skilled fire-fighters from the picture-book riverside village. His men were dry, warm, and ready.

That was a triumph for Tom Edwards because he was the leading light in foreseeing the future for fire engines – and persuading the loyal village people to raise the money so that it could be built by Markham's, the well-known Reading body-builders.

Equally dedicated, if not as warm, were AFS from Newbury and Wokingham, somewhere in that melee of pumps congregating for action.

A dozen pumps were together in Gordon's group mustered at West Drayton. A London fire officer led them through London, all along by the Thames. It was a terrible mess. Lines of hose were everywhere, 'It's like a great cobweb,' he said as they bumped over and onward.

A feeling of bewilderment hit him as he reached the docks. Maybe some firefighters has seen fires of such intensity but never so overwhelming. 'What do we do with this lot?' he said to himself.

*   *   *

The pump crews fighting the fires, at the Docks from the start, were badly in need of relief. 'Most of them are dead out on their feet,' Ken told his crew when he came back from being marshalled where to take over. 'Remember how tough you find it holding on to a highly charged branch for an ordinary fire? Well these men have been hanging on to their hose lines since 5 pm, and it's now nearly 11. Six hours of fire fighting against a conflagration, with bombs crashing around all the time.'

The London crew, which Caversham were to relieve, could hardly manage a smile, but it was clear how pleased they were to see them. Their's was a vitally important self-propelled pump, and they wanted to take it back to their station with them – and they were in no fit state to tramp back in rubber boots, with wet and blistered feet.

Bombs were still crashing down, machine guns adding their deadly chatter, it really was as light as day. A dreadful new experience, everyone felt so vulnerable. It was as if the bombers' gunners were aiming at them!

'We will go and fetch our own pump,' said Ken. Off they went to find it. Hauling and pushing, they manhandled it over the debris, at last reaching the London crew. Two or three were already fast asleep.

It was then that Ken learnt first hand that the equipment on their new Home Office pump was useless for London hydrants! Their standpipes would not fit, to connect to the mains, and their hose would not connect to London's screw-thread standpipes, so water could not reach their pump! 'My God, is this going to be the case in all the cities?' He was to find that to be the case in many big provincial towns.

'Right, we will keep the London boys standpipe and hose and use our own pump,' snapped Ken. 'We will leave them by the hydrant when we have finished,' he told the exhausted men. Nodding agreement, the London firemen wished them 'Good luck' and were away. But not before they warned Ken of the whereabouts of the delayed action bombs which had fallen while they were at the fire.

Ken put the part-timer in charge of the pump, and the rest of them went off to the fire. Their branches were throwing out powerful jets of water, a solid stream of water for 150 feet. 'Talk about David and Goliath,' Ken said. Containers of incendiaries were dropping out of the sky, opening and spilling 36 foot-long bombs, which in turn were sending out glittering showers of white splinters of magnesium.

For a while Ken and the others were perched on a wall about six feet high. As they got used to the inferno, they realised it was not a wall but all that remained of one of the warehouses. Sitting with their legs astride, they were forcing the jet of water into the fire below. Below was the right word, because the whole structure, walls, floors, and contents, had collapsed into what had been the basement.

There was fear, but there was no time for fear!

They stuck at it. After a time, Ken realised that railway trucks behind them had caught fire from flying embers and radiated heat. As he investigated, he found that, strangely, they were filled with rubber-lined hose. It had survived the torpedoes of the U-boats, as a freighter had battled across the Atlantic, all the way from America?

'We could use our jet to good advantage and save a lot of that hose,' thought Ken. He was prophetic again, little did he know how precious such hose was going to be in a year or so. It seemed sense, they were not going to save anything in the warehouse.

With one or two other crews, he had just started carrying out the intention when a senior officer demanded to know 'What are you doing?' When told, he said, 'Turn your jets back into the warehouse.'

Retelling the story back in Reading, Ken said, 'We were only rookies I know but commonsense convinces me we could have saved 70 per cent of that hose. But, orders are orders, we obeyed the instruction and the trucks were allowed to burn out.'

As night turned to morning in the docks, the crews found the water supply becoming acutely short. Other firemen set up big sportapools, flat round canvas dams, and kept these filled with lines of hose bringing water from somewhere else in the docks. Ken, and the other crews, set their pumps into these and carried on the fight.

Suddenly with an awful noise one of the DA's – they were learning the language in record time – went off. Then another. Ken checked round his crew, fortunately there were still no casualties.

As they all fought on, there was another scream and down came a high explosive bomb. It dropped in a side road opposite the dock gates. A large gap appeared where there had been rows of terraced back-to-back houses but, again no casualties, Lady Luck seemed to be on their side.

Wherever the water was coming from it was still keeping the crews supplied. Ken went back to speak to his pump operator, checking the pressure and warning gauges to make sure all was well. Every jet of water was vital to try and get the flames under control; they were a beacon of immense proportions to any and every enemy plane.

Suddenly along the street, in the middle of the maelstrom, a middle-aged woman

– a real East-Ender, the people London was to learn to be proud of – carrying a large wash-stand jug. Beside her was a little kiddie, 'She can only be four or five,' thought Ken, clutching a handful of tin mugs.

She came up to the fireman and said, 'Would you chaps like some tea?' 'Yes, please,' all replied, suddenly realising just how dry their throats were in the gasping heat and smoke. Putting the jug down amid the debris on the pavement, she took one of the cups from the child and carefully wiped it in her apron. She took the others and wiped them as well, oblivious to the hell around her, and then poured out the tea.

'Never did tea taste better or sweeter,' Ken told her as all the crew gasped their thanks. 'But, why are you out with your child in the middle of a blitz?' She shrugged her shoulders – 'I thought the men would like a drink. They must be thirsty with all that heat.'

She took the cups and, with the child at her side, set off towards the dock gates, there to offer her tea to any man she saw.

Neither mum nor child showed the slightest signs of fear. 'It's a pity Goering can't see her, his much-vaunted Luftwaffe has certainly failed to frighten these East-Enders,' said Ken out loud. It was as though he was shouting to Germany, telling the Nazis they can't win.

Back home, trying to return to a normal life, especially when off duty and hairdressing to help dad, Ken kept wondering, 'Where the hell did she get the water, and heat the kettle, with both the water and gas mains gone? It was a memory he was never to forget.

There was another as the night wore on. During a brief lull in the bombing, another East-Ender, this time a man, came up to Ken. 'Would you like a glass of beer?' 'Yes, very much,' replied Ken, 'but I have some pals who would too.' 'Come with me,' and led the firemen into a house a few doors down a side street. They were welcomed into a small room, which already had about ten people in it.

On the table were two bottles of beer and three cups, and it was all given to the firemen. When Ken offered to pay, he realised that he had seriously offended these good people. It needed all his charm to rescue the situation, as they sat and chatted for a quarter of an hour.

The women in the room looked a little frightened, not because of the bombing, it was the thought of losing their homes! Ken, like Tom, was a Londoner born and bred, but in that holocaust he came to realise that he had never known before what grand people were the East-Enders, and what guts they had.

Finally, that Sunday morning, the raiders turned for home. 'Evidently they are satisfied with their night's devilry,' said Ken. The All Clear, sounded, Ken thought it was about 5.30 am, but he was too tired to bother to look.

Presently, from the various rows of houses and buildings, people began to appear and gaze at the sky. Clouds of acrid smoke and steam, were rising from the docks, it was a sight that few in Britain could ever have dreamed of. Those few were the people who pressed on and provided all the fire pumps in case . . . , whilst the majority hoped that war would go away. Ken shook his head as he thought about it.

62

Miraculously, the newspapers appeared! A typical Cockney was standing close by Ken when, buying his paper and opening it, he saw the headlines telling of the East End's night of bombing. He turned to Ken and, with a smile, said, in his chirpy language, 'Blimey, they're telling us!' He hadn't lost his Cockney wit.

Shortly after came the message that Ken and his crew would be relieved about 9 am. 'Some fresh crews are already coming in, so that the tired ones,' he laughed as he told his men that, 'can leave for their home stations.'

Sure enough at 9.30 am their relief crew arrived. Ken and his men set to with the final back-breaking task of rescuing and rolling up their hose, and packing their gear back on the pump. Even rolling hose was a dangerous and new experience. Everywhere tiny slivers of glass were imbedded in the hose, waiting to cut a fireman's hands. Punctured hose was to prove a big headache in the future.

On their way back to Whitechapel they had ample chance to view the damage which had been caused all around them during the darkness, by HE and incendiary bombs, not forgetting the landmines and aerial torpedoes which added to the terror.

It was 11.30 am when Ken reported to Whitechapel and his crew were dismissed to go home to Caversham. As they started for home, they heard the wail of the siren as it started again!

It was an unforgettable sight as mothers came from the tenement flats carrying, or leading, their children and babies, hurrying to the shelters before it all began again. Fortunately, it was a false alarm, and the bombers did not return until the evening. When they did the bombers killed 412 civilians and injured 747 seriously.

As Ken drove home, his crew saw other firemen in convoys still heading in to London to help. For the first time they had the feeling that they had done a really useful job of work, had been tried and not found wanting.

'Do you realise,' he mused, 'we have seen, and fought, fires the size of which no brass hat has ever seen the like of before? We aren't second class any longer.'

He was right. No longer could the men on the red machines – which the Corporation refused to allow out of the town to the blitz – claim superior knowledge and experience. No longer would the vicious tongues of women claiming firemen were trying to dodge the fighting, ever wag again.

Back at Caversham action station, the stories had to wait as the routines took precedence. Ken knew now how right he was to make sure they were always ready. Log books were filled in, pump and Packard checked and filled with petrol, oil and water. Fresh hose was put on the pump, the original put to be scrubbed, dried and checked.

Instructions were issued to the stand-by crews, and then home for the warriors. 'Go and get some grub and sleep,' Ken told them. Their last substantial meal had been midday on Saturday, and their last sleep, Friday night.

Lucy was waiting to welcome him, trying not to show her worry. She did not tell him how she had gone to the station to find out what was happening, as she had seen them dash away without a chance to say a word of Goodbye.

'Did you know the stations were asked for second regional crews to stand by?' Lucy could not help telling Ken, although she wanted him to unwind from such an incredible experience. 'It was just an hour after you left,' she explained. 'The off-duty crews were recalled – they wanted to know if the station was still manned when you left, John said 'Yes'. The siren warning lasted until 4.30 am, and then it was sounded again by mistake! Your part-timers stayed on duty in the morning.'

Ken was back at the station almost as soon as he awoke with the sirens sounding at 8.20 pm. There he was told of the repercussion in the town; how reinforcing crews had been called from even farther across the country, to stand-by to help cover Reading, and to go on into London if deemed necessary.

'Such was the lack of organisation,' John told him, 'that men had to sleep on the Promenade, under the river bridges, and others in their towing vehicles. Feeding facilities were haywire, and a good many had no food at all!' 'By God, we have got a lot to learn,' said Ken.

Excitement was running high as Ken recounted the details to the other men. 'The raid kept on until about 4.30 on the Sunday morning. Never before has any fire service faced such a terrific task as the London Brigade did that night,' he told them. 'They had to tackle nine conflagrations – and that's a new word for us to think about, huge areas with flames spreading in all directions!'

There were a few choice expletives as the picture sank in. 'But that's not all, they also had huge fires which, in peace time, would have been fought with 40 or more pumps.'

There was a natural nervousness related to the excitement. All were on tenter-hooks, waiting and wondering when the next call would come. It seemed difficult to settle into the normal routine, making sure everything was still on absolute top line.

Roger with his Tilehurst crew were the last to return home. He had not escaped unscathed. 'Sorry, we have damage to the car' – he was quite attached to RD 5570 – 'and No 5 pump has its brake broken and the petrol tank is leaking.'

*   *   *

'What do we do with this lot?' The same question as Gordon was mouthing was being asked by the Buckinghamshire AFS men, for a different reason. All six of the ex-railway vans were ordered to London. Five of them broke down on the way, one kept going. That crew worked all night to save one of the city's big landmarks.

Their efforts were recognised and people were keeping them 'fit' with little bottles of whisky and other pleasant things. Dirty as they were, breakfast was in the BBC's restaurant. But, things were obviously going too well for them – on the way home they broke down! The sixth and last!

*   *   *

Although London continued to be bombed, Caversham received no further calls immediately, nor did the other local stations. The London Fire Brigade, having recovered from the first sledge-hammer attack, was ready to meet further onslaughts.

The major daylight attacks – 200 to 300 bombers at a time – were hitting the docks and installations hard. But the Germans were suffering too, as fighters and guns fought back.

There was no respite either for the AFS: seemingly never-ending alerts, big demands by street groups for stirrup pump training, even spraying paraffin oil on emergency dams of water to prevent mosquitos spreading diseases. Woodley aerodrome was again a target.

The buzzes started when the top brass of the Government's ARP for 'district 9', the HM fire inspector, and the chief officers of all its brigades, met at headquarters. 'They must be very worried,' whispered Ken to John.

It was only four days after special messages had been circulated to station officers: 'During the last two nights a number of suspected magnetic mines have been dropped by parachute in urban areas. Many unexploded. Admiralty investigating and advise, NO metal, not even tin hats or tools be brought near. All vibration should be avoided in the vicinity. Evacuation as for large unexploded bombs'. Second came, 'Look out for small containers, containing liquid and phosphorous pellets. These may be used to fire heath and woodlands'.

Already there had been a strange coincidence of a woodland fire started by enemy action at Woodley aerodrome. Sonning's volunteer brigade had reported that. That was the day before a stick of bombs by a petrol station there.

Two days after the 'secret' meeting incendiaries and high-explosives started fires at Bracknell, while a 500-pounder thankfully missed The Crown, at Basildon. Roger and his crew were called to stand by for an unexploded land mine which dropped there. Fire bombs dropped at Henley on several nights, and DAs at South Ascot. Some exploded and fire spread for two miles alongside the railway, and the Army sent 200 men to help fight it because of the danger.

'September 27 saw the last of the big daylight raids,' Ken wrote in his diary. Although not called to London he was feeling for the people every day. 'But not the night raids,' he added later. 'It was hell on September 30, and there was only one night's respite until November 13!'

That Monday, the raiders came to Reading as 200 planes scattered across the South East. That night in London it was the heaviest raid yet. As a prelude, there had been a mass attack on the docks at teatime. Then it really started, just after 8 pm and went on to 5 am. Between five and eight raids were continually in progress, who could tell how many?

Tom Goldsmid had his version. He heard, he said, 'the Jerries had 1,000 planes crossing the coast at one time. Twenty squadrons of fighters went to meet them.' To make sure he was believed, he added, 'My friends still in London could see the air fights.'

During September 5,730 people were killed and nearly 10,000 badly injured.

October started locally with a plane down at Checkendon and more bombs on Woodley 'drome. A fireman reporting on duty at Tilehurst told Roger, 'I can see a fire after hearing bombs exploding.' 'It's out of our area at Woodley,' replied Roger, telling him of the attack on the aerodrome. Reading and the aerodrome were to continue to be targets, but not of mass attacks, until the grim winter weather prevented the raiders from taking off from their hurriedly improvised French bases.

10 · Coventrate!

When, during October, the Germans shifted their main attacks to night raids only, it must be because of their losses, presumed Ken Watson. It was a small relief, time to return to improving preparations and conditions at his station, just as was happening at all action stations. The council workmen were even getting round to fitting permanent black-out at the Oxford Road station!

There were some mighty tired men about; not forgetting the part-timers who were losing so much sleep regularly at night and still having their other war work to do during the day.

It was clear to Ken that an important feature of the enemy's tactics was to spread raids over as long a time, and as wide an area, as possible. 'They are thinking of us especially, I think,' Ken said to John Lander. 'Just the same way as they are slinging down the heavy high explosive bombs at the beginning of raids to bust up the water mains. They want us to lose heart.'

There was no time to sit and lose heart. The Luftwaffe targeted ports and factories frantically replacing munitions lost in France and at Dunkirk. Nuisance raids were going on around all the time but, as October closed Birmingham was the principal target in the Midlands. Raids were also on other cities, including Liverpool and Coventry, and Reading.

As November came the bombers finally switched from London to widen their hits on other vital cities and towns. Later Ken was to write '23 major Luftwaffe attacks across the country this month. Can it go on?' But before he put pen to paper the AFS were on the move again.

Firework night – 'That's a laugh to remember those festivities,' said Ken as he stood with his men on full alert in the early evening. It seemed the raiders were heading for Reading and Newbury. All night long the sirens were wailing on and off.

Suddenly, raids on Coventry took on a new meaning.

Factories working for the war effort, particularly those feverishly building fighter planes to replace those lost in the battles, had to be saved if humanly possible. Men were sent from Reading to Coventry as reliefs, as the city repeatedly became the target of the raiders. The fire-fighters stayed for four or five days and, on return, fresh men took their place.

Home for these men in Coventry was the 'Spike' as they called it, the workhouse. It was talked about for its 'blessed great sandwiches, with tomato and cheese'. Each man was given one before the night raids started. When the sirens sounded they were sent to various action stations as reinforcements. Before long, all the full-time men at Caversham, and the other stations in the town, could claim blitz experience. It was the same for AFS men in many 'quiet' towns throughout the country, all were ready and willing to back up colleagues pushed to their limits.

There was a rebuke for one crew who, faced with a rainstorm of incendiaries, grabbed sandbags from around a shelter to snuff them out. A city officer tore them off a strip, 'You are using sandbags put there for the protection of life. There are plenty of chrysanthemums growing in that garden, you could have pulled up and slapped on.'

'Although no one enjoyed facing such fury in Coventry, or Birmingham, I can truthfully say that not one of my men was scared,' Ken proudly told the local LDV commander, as they chatted over their respective problems.

Gordon Castle's men were a little more careful with their choice of words. They were just back from Coventry. The city had suffered raids every night they were there. One dark night, which was a strange twist as most were in moonlight, Gordon and his crew were ordered to another fire started by the bombers. Not knowing the way, a despatch rider led. It was a brave duty which the DRs were performing night after night. Driving through the hazards, the motor cyclist suddenly disappeared! He had ridden straight into a bomb crater.

'What the devil's happened to him?' was Gordon first shout. Braking hard, he suddenly realised that their taxi was on the edge of the hole. Until then they had no idea of the danger, and would have gone in but for his misfortune. Scrambling down, they dragged him out shaken but not badly hurt. 'Blimey, that wasn't there half and hour ago,' was all he could say.

Gordon, himself, saw a horror sight, which shocked him. Close to where they were fire fighting, were brick-built air raid shelters in the road – a common protection. Many of Reading's streets were reduced to half-width by them. A high-explosive bomb hit one of the shelters, and 50 or more people were killed in it.

'I swore then that never again would I stay in a building when there is a raid on,' he told Ken the next time they met.

During the following days of continuing blitzing the thoughts of all the men were with their fellow AFS who were in the city. Ken, and his fellow action station controlling officers, were nervous with excitement as they wondered why the reinforcements call did not come. 'I am sure it is because of the number of men we have already away from our stations,' said Ken. 'It has left Reading dangerously undermanned. Who knows which town will be next?'

Then, on the night of the 14th, came the raid which was to put a new word, Coventrate, into the English language. The cathedral was destroyed, and there was a new anger across the country as Britain stood alone. A full moon shone brightly over the city. Bombers' machine-gunners aimed for the fire-fighters, illuminated and defenceless, as they fought the fires the bombs had started.

At first Caversham was not called on as additional crews were sent to relieve. It was evening when, at last, the telephone gave the message 'Stand by'. A few minutes later, it was 'Move'. Away went Caversham's pump and men, with their trusty Packard, just as was happening elsewhere. Ken stayed at the station, it was John's turn to take the responsibility. 'Get your heads down, get some sleep while you can,' he told those left holding the fort. That did not last long before the first purple was received.

For the weary, red-eyed, firemen in the city there was to be no All Clear – even the sirens were out of action. Just like the anti-aircraft guns, silent out of ammunition.

It was a night no one was going to forget as the bombers droned continuously over Reading, indeed a wide swathe of England as they headed north, with that breathtaking, frightening hunting note to the engines. Part-timers, and messengers, got out their cycles and rushed to the fire stations, called by the warning sirens, as the bombers first approached the Thames Valley.

Often part-timers found empty fire stations, with doors wide open, where the full-time AFS men had set off for Coventry in answer to the desperate call for aid. Quickly they manned more appliances. When the All Clear sounded they stayed on to provide extra cover. Nobody ever knew when another switched attack would strike their town – the Germans were clever, they attacked one place and, while that was in uproar, more bombers came and hit another target.

Ken had been driving to Coventry one night when that happened. They were on the road and out-of-touch when the bombers switched to Birmingham. Hitler's men knew they had got the firemen into the wrong place.

Sirens were sounding so regularly night after night, and often lasting from dusk to dawn. The most precious loss was sleep. A far bigger worry, even, than trying to think what to bring to eat. For the part-time men, and messengers, had to be fit for 'normal' work the next day, while the full-time men needed to be alert for the station routine, and maintenance, monotonous but essential.

Sleep often had to be put to the back of one's mind, red alert or no alert. One night Ken was faced with a dilemma when one of the pumps would not start. At this time every unit was critical – just in case. Those who normally looked after the machines could not solve it. When, part-time fireman Ray came on duty, they were quick to seek his advice. He was a professional motor engineer. It could not be started, so he set to and spent most of the night repairing it, then off to work as usual in the morning. No wonder Ken proudly used to tell outsiders, 'These men really are men.'

By now Ken had seven pumps at the station, two large and five light. It was the station boast that it always had sufficient men to man them. Policy was to hold one full-time crew for blitz calls, while the others were made up of a couple of full-timers, with blitz experience, and the keen part-timers.

During the long winter nights, these men were to suffer considerable discomfort as they stood ready and waiting for action. There had been no cheers, when earlier in the year, Ken told his men of the changed policy which meant dispersing all pumps when the alarm was given. 'One hit on our station and all would be out of action,' Ken told them. This time he agreed with the move.

The men knew it made sense but were not enamoured when they set off for action points, often sheds or garages, sometimes just stopping at cross roads!

As the winter came, the station's small patrol car took round tea to them. Reports would come back to Ken of men huddled up in their vehicles, very, very, cold but

68

always cheerful. The men took it in turns to stand outside and keep a watchful eye on the sky, and also to keep in contact with the nearest wardens' post for instructions.

Often the phone in the station would ring as an alert fireman gave information on flares, and glows in the sky, invaluable useful information as Ken tried to guess if enemy action was nearing his area. 'If only radio really worked and there were a lot more telephones,' he sighed one night to John. His messenger on duty that night was within earshot and, to himself, he grunted in agreement – there were too many hills in Caversham for fast cycling!

Sometimes, if the glare was near, a crew would be ordered to go and investigate. More often than not it proved to be a few incendiaries dropped as a 'feeler'. Ken and his men soon got used to the peculiar flickering light they gave off from a distance.

At least the action gave some warmth. In the depth of the winter, when the alerts seemed never ending, crews would be ordered back at intervals to spend half-an-hour thawing out around the boiler. Life was proving tough, even when the bombers did not come to a particular town, or indeed village. 'And to think the vast majority of these people are not paid a penny,' said Ken to John. 'They are volunteers.'

*   *   *

John was still thinking about his experiences in the blitzes on Coventry. Quite a few Coventry fire-fighters were killed. 'It's going to be a pretty rotten Christmas for their kiddies, fatherless, and some are homeless as well,' he said. 'Why can't we get some toys together. I know there is nothing new about but we could make an appeal.'

'Let us see if we can get permission,' said Ken. He did, and they did.

Placards and a box outside the station entrance had no effect. It seemed the people were all too tired to bother, or had nothing decent left to give.

In despair, they decided to make public appeals. Both cinemas, the Regal and the Caversham Electric, gave permission for John to speak from the stage, three nights in succession. The vicar at St Peter's, right next door, to the action station, read the appeal from his pulpit the next Sunday, with Ken standing by. It was mentioned at the demonstrations the firemen were giving to teach people how to use stirrup pumps.

By Monday evening, when John went to the box it was already half full. Over the next fortnight, all kinds of gifts arrived, not only were there the hoped for part-worn but useful toys, but brand new ones, books and clothing. 'The people of Caversham have responded magnificently,' said John.

Just before Christmas the firemen sent to Coventry a two-ton lorry full of gifts, and £28 in cash, a lot of money in those starved days.

All were certain this would bring a little happiness into some of the homes. Judging by the letter received from Coventry, which Ken pinned up for public view outside the station, it was much appreciated. The £28, they were told, had been distributed by the Coventry Fire Brigade amongst the widows of their men.

*   *   *

'It was Birmingham that took another beating last night,' Ken told John. 'Remember the night the air raid wardens stopped us just outside Brum? They could hardly speak they were so full of emotion, as they wished us 'Good luck, and God speed'.'

'Remember, too, that eye-witness account we were given when we got there?' said John. 'The fire engine tearing down the road with its bell ringing. A bomb fell right in front and the engine, with its crew, and dead man's hand still ringing the bell, rose into the air and disintegrated.'

Both stood quietly, there seemed nothing else to say.

November the 19th was the night the might of the Germans concentrated on Birmingham, with its vital war factories. Without doubt they were again trying to beat people into submission. For 11 hours its centre bore the brunt of effective concentrated bombing. Railways, telephones, all the services were badly hit. Hundreds were dead or injured.

So bad was the state that calls were put out to a huge area of the country calling for firemen as reinforcements. Reading was among them. So was London, repaying a debt, 60 pumps were sent. Tom Goldsmid brought that news. 'Three hundred fires by early evening,' he reckoned.

Water was a desperate problem. Already suffering from busted pipes on previous raids, now the big trunk mains were broken, including the critical huge supply coming all the way from the Elan Valley in Wales. It was to become a city without water!

Gordon was to remember it as the worst time he had. Again he was both in charge and the driver of his pump. By now he knew his way fairly well. They went to work on the BSA works. A local fire officer reckoned there were 600 fires the last time he heard.

It was a vital factory to save and Gordon joined a line of pumps relaying water from the Warwick and Birmingham Canal. It was the only 'ammunition' there was for their 'guns', the pumps. So much was needed that the canal was pumped almost dry.

Gordon was switched to running relays from swimming pools and lakes, over a couple of miles away. For three days and three nights, with his crew, he was there. Hardly any food, just a few sandwiches, conditions in the city were stretched to breaking point.

Relieved, he headed for Reading. It was dark again by the time he reached his home station. 'Good, now we can go home,' he said to the others.

A senior officer was holding the fort. As they drove in the sirens sounded. The other pumps were scrambling away to their action points. 'You have been out all this time, you had better stay here,' he said.

'Good,' said Gordon, 'I'm going over the road to the pub for a pint.' That pint

70

was not to be, it was just put on the counter when a messenger came in, 'They want you back at the station.'

The other officer said, 'I have got to send a pump to Birmingham. We cannot contact the others, and you are the only driver. You will have to go again.' In the calm light of a pre-war peaceful day's routine it would have been unbelievable. But not in 1940. Gordon did not protest. 'OK,' he said – still thinking about that thirst-quenching pint going flat on the pub counter.

Gordon felt so tired, he could not keep awake. By the time he reached Stratford-on-Avon he was dozing off as he drove. One of the crew realising the danger said he would have a go. He had never driven before but he took them to Birmingham while Gordon slept flat out.

When they reached the city, refreshed, he took over. They were sent to the Lycett saddle works, but it was a lost battle. There was little water and the factory was burnt out. Again they were there for three days; wet through, Gordon's clothes dried on him, there was not even a chance to take his boots off, his socks had shrivelled on his feet. That was how bad it was.

It was worse even than the time when Gordon found himself fighting a fire which did not exist! Called to a house which was still smoking badly, fired by an incendiary,, Gordon went in with a hose. Playing it into the heart of the brightness he could see dimly.

From below, a voice came clearly, 'That's a daft idea having that light on.' and it was switched off. The 'fire' disappeared, and Gordon realised he was standing on the very edge of a huge hole in the bedroom floor.

As they fought more fires, one of Gordon's crew leant back against a wall, trying to ease his physical agony. Propped against a drainpipe he slowly slid down to the pavement – fast asleep! He was not the only one to sleep on his feet.

Back home, Gordon's wife was in mental agony. He had been away for almost a week, without any news from him. All she knew was together with many others he was in danger, in the front line.

*   *   *

Home at last night, Gordon was flat out when he dragged himself into bed. He never heard the siren. It was the first time he had missed turning out. His wife let him sleep on – 'Let them do without him,' she said quietly, with feeling.

Suddenly there was a terrific whump, the shaking of the bed woke Gordon. The flap of a cabinet downstairs dropped down with another crash. Somehow, in a flash he was wide awake. 'Keep still, there are some more coming,' he whispered. And the ground shook again.

He laid back, exhausted with just that effort. But not for long. Tap, tap, tap, on the front door. It was a warden. 'Everybody out, unexploded bombs.' 'That's funny, I have never known an UXB which moved my bed like that,' said Gordon. 'They must have gone off.'

He was not leaving, he told the warden. 'I will take my wife and baby into the back of the house, and put the baby under the table.' It was not long before a policeman arrived and said, 'You have got to get out.'

Borrowing a car, he took his wife, child, and their evacuee, to the safety of his mother's house. When they returned the warden said, 'You were right, they had all gone off.' To prove it, there were holes in that Whitley Wood field which would take a double-decker bus. They were a stone's throw from Gordon's house and did not break a pane of glass!

11 · To the coast

The new blackboard was fixed to the wall of the tiny office at the Oxford Road station. Similar boards had gone up in the other stations. Simple and quite smart really, round discs on hooks denoted the fire pumps and written in chalk alongside each, where it was and who were the crew. 'That's it in black and white,' thought Roger Smith. It tells the story of all of us.

Other AFS men saw the action with similar great clarity, part-timers as well as the men who signed on full-time when asked a year earlier. A year ago? How the world had changed? Now the shopkeepers and artisans of Britain were listed, routinely, as 'Regional crew' and 'Stand-by regional crew'.

First and second line of defence, all ready to ride to help those suffering at the hands of the villain. Almost pantomime, well it seemed like that quite often. The rest would stay at home in case the villain came to visit them.

Portsmouth, when it suffered its first major raid in August, then the ferocity of the attacks on London, had put new meaning into being ready. By November all firemen needed a board on the wall.

Roger watched the tension mount. Just gone 10 pm on a November Tuesday night, the phone rang. 'Two crews stand-by for regional call.' The sirens had sounded four-and-a-half-hours earlier and the call put a jerk into the tedium for the few still at the station. The ready-and-waiting regional crew were kept at the fire station. The 'seconds' were spread with pumps at the action points.

Off went the Morris Ten to bring them back. Just think, a couple of years earlier the station officer used to go racing in it. What a different life now?

More petrol was poured into the one standing by to go on a long journey. Where? They could guess. Three-quarters-of-an-hour later they had the answer. 'RD5570 and No 5 pump to Birmingham.'

Another two hours, then, 'Dismiss second regional crew.' A sense of hidden relief ran through those men. Almost immediately the All Clear sounded. The lorries started to arrive back, the unloading started again.

Two days later the five men came back from Birmingham.

The next night, an hour earlier, No 5 pump was off to Birmingham again, different men in the crew.

Exactly the same time the following night, men were called to go to Southampton. With men still at Birmingham, they were stretched! Five men took a pump, with a temporary promotion to leading fireman for one of them.

Sunday: 9.5 am, another call for Birmingham! Three men go, three full-timers are left on duty. 'It's all going to rely on the part-timers if they hit Reading,' said Roger, the man left in charge.

The Southampton crew were back first, the five toiling in Birmingham since Friday arrived at tea-time. The other stations were under the same pressure. Then, nearing midnight, the last three from Birmingham were back as well. A purple warning kept everyone on duty, on their toes.

Quarter to one in the morning, the telephone rang. Everybody went tense, 'What now?' The three crew just back were to report to the central station at 7.45 am to go to Bristol. No let up, five minutes later, the patrol officer, who would lead them, was taking his turn on guard. So regular were the calls that the 'locals' began travelling in convoy. This time they were back in an hour. That was a relief.

Tuesday evening, 26th, bombs on Caversham. This time the action stations were helping their own. Tilehurst to the Oratory School, taken over and vital for BBC broadcasting; South to Hemdean road and the library; the red engines to Prospect Street. Eastern as well, they were all there to reinforce Ken Watson and his Caversham men.

Sending men to blitz by bus was introduced. Four from Tilehurst were in the party which left for Southampton on Thursday.

'Regional crew to Southampton IMMEDIATELY,' There was a purple warning on when the message, with its new emphasis, came at 8.15 pm on Saturday, the last day of November. They were back at tea-time on Sunday, their pump had been working 10½ hours continuously. Four hours later, another call for Tilehurst. It was logged 20.55: 'Pump and crew to Southampton by 21.00.' It did not take five minutes, one man was fetched from home and they were off in three, with their station officer in charge. It did take them until Wednesday to get back home, with a lot of pumping time recorded.

So the calls went on for Tilehurst, for all the stations: Saturday, Fareham until Friday; Sunday, Southampton – for a week; the next was mysterious, it said 'Five men to HQ' – it turned out to be Southampton again. Late Sunday, a crew was recalled from an action point to be ready to go – 2½ hours later they were stood down.

Christmas was getting near. On the Eve, five were off to Stockport.

Later in the morning the Chief Officer came to the Tilehurst station to bring a notice of 'Thanks for services rendered by the depot at Southampton.' The response of the AFS men was appreciated by those being mauled. 'All the depots must be getting one of these,' said Roger.

It was quiet on Christmas Day but not for the men at Stockport, they did not get home until Boxing Day. Next call was to Exeter but, after standing ready for seven hours, it was cancelled. Sunday, the 29th, 'Crew for long-distance call.' Looking at the skyline they all knew that meant London.

So into the New Year: Bristol (and burst pump petrol tank!). The sirens seemed to laugh as they sounded at the same moment as they got back.

Next morning, Sunday, 'All men resting, patrol officer on guard,' was the laconic entry which spoke volumes.

The Chief Officer telephoned to check how many part-time men were available.

Earlier he had checked on the number of messengers as well. Messenger Len Hall was pleased at that. His job was in a men's outfitters, but he seemed to be always on duty. Someone at the shop was turning a blind eye, in true Nelson fashion. Len was proving important, one small vital task was calling men from home to make up the regional crews – or when they slept through a siren. Not always the most popular!

Next two were for Fareham, a stand-by base was established there, ready to move in to Portsmouth, Southampton, Bournemouth? Wherever needed.

At exactly the same moment on Sunday, one crew left for Gosport as another arrived back from Fareham, with a casualty, glass in his hand which needed the hospital and stitches. A little later the others were also back from Fareham.

Next, the 13th, call for help from Plymouth, 'Go to Exeter,' was the message. At the same time, 1,000 sandbags were being delivered and a load of sand dumped outside. It was for their own station's protection. 'There is going to be no let up,' said Roger.

*　　*　　*

'Two lorries have gone to Bristol taking mobile dams, one is from Wokingham,' John Lander told Ken Watson. By then, life was full of alerts, calls, and 'buzzes'. It was only five frantic days since Caversham, Tilehurst, and East, had returned from Birmingham.

Three days later Reading AFS were sent by bus back to the city. Five units from Bournemouth passed through, stopping long enough for a breather, answering one of the blitz pleas. Five from London came later, heading in another direction. Oxford AFS stopped off with dams they were taking to Southampton. It was all happening, all the time.

Bristol had been a tough task. Even as a port with waterways into the centre a shortage of 'ammunition' had been a major problem – also for the people living there who had to collect drinking water from handcarts and tankers brought in. At least the fire service had a head start in calling for reinforcements.

Gordon Castle's chaps back from Bristol had a strange story to tell. 'We got a call to Bath, two o'clock in the afternoon, as you know. 'We thought, that's funny there's nothing wrong here! Why the devil have we come to Bath?

'At 5 pm the siren went, the raid was on Bristol. Our intelligence must have known there was going to be a raid there, otherwise, why send us to Bath?' the leading fireman shook his head. He was right but he did not know it! 'It was a bad night, churches, schools, and the shops, took a hammering. Fifty, may be more, were in a shelter which was hit. A lot died that night.'

*　　*　　*

Gordon Castle admired his fellow AFS. So too, did he the drivers of the lorries they 'borrowed' every night to guard their own town. Rough old lorries some of them, which only their own employees were supposed to drive. Not so, the Joynes, builders merchants' vehicle, that was 'beautiful' – and one of the AFS had driven it himself when he worked for the firm before the war! Geoff Love's builder's lorry was another of the warhorses.

*   *   *

The day came when Caversham's men realised they were really looking after their own patch. Poetically Ken and his men were taking apart German incendiary bombs brought back from Southampton, to give realism to a drill for local stirrup pump parties. Outside the civic centre in the port, a special constable was watching big pails full of IBs, standing up just like flowers. He clearly wanted to get rid of them, so Ken put them in the back of the Packard and took them home.

Clamped in a vice, the skids and fins were taken off. Unscrewing the head, they took out the detonator, they were almost ready for the practice when, John said, 'Hark, that sounds like a Jerry!' 'He won't touch us, we've got a red cross on the roof,' quipped Ken.

No sooner said, the joke fell flat as incendiary bombs clattered down into the forecourt by the vehicles. The raider had launched high explosives and a container of incendiaries, spreading its bombs across Caversham. Into the Thames, a hedge in Caversham Court, shed in St Peter's Hill, through the roof of a house in St Anne's Road, and so on, the last reaching the far side of the suburb, in the Welsh colony, off Henley Road.

'They're coming down like rain drops,' shouted someone as they all swung into action. It was not long before the telephone rang. 'Why did you not tell me about these bombs,' shouted the Chief Officer. 'Well, you said we were on our own,' replied Ken. 'Well get used to using the telephone,' was the acid reply.

*   *   *

When Ken picked his first crews to drive out into the beginnings of this Southampton blitz, he knew they would be going to docks and warehouses. Most appliances were sent there, to safeguard the precious stocks which had been shipped in escaping the U-boats. Also, knowing that the dock areas were always very congested and the danger of fires spreading was great. Ken still remembered vividly that first baptism at London's East India Docks.

This night proved to be bad luck for fire guards defending one of the docks' great warehouses. Three times incendiaries showered on to the building. On the first and second occasions all were extinguished by their valiant efforts. But the third time, a near miss by an accompanying high explosive bomb destroyed their water supply and they had to retreat helpless.

The warehouse stored tobacco, with rum underneath in the vaults. The whole building was involved and, two days later, with some of the rum barrels exploding, tobacco still smouldering, all the floors had collapsed.

A decision was made to flood the basement, so that the rest of the rum could be saved. Ken was given the job. Fifteen one-inch jets were turned on to the still burning tobacco. Every minute thousands of gallons of water was flowing through the debris and tobacco into the vaults.

Several of the branch men pouring in the water were ordered to move. 'Get to places of safety,' ordered Ken, as one of the walls began cracking ominously. 'If that falls it will engulf you!' The men pulled back but did not ease up on the vital gallons each was pouring into the building.

Step by step the water gradually rose in the basement then, a dark brown stream began flowing into the gutters – the nicotine was leaving its mark. When, eventually, the fire was cooled down the men had to reverse their work and pump out the vaults. There the rum was found to have survived and was salvaged.

A strange sight met Ken's eyes as the flooding was going on. Several firemen walking by seemed to have grown massive chests! Investigating he found that they had dozens of tobacco leaves wrapped around them. A sailor had told them that the leaves could be dried, wrapped in paper, placed in a drawer and, in three months, would mature.

These chaps had fallen for his 'advice' and were trying to get the leaves home. Looting was punishable but Ken, quietly laughing to himself, turned a blind eye. They had been through a lot and he realised that the leaves would be mouldy within weeks.

Early in the raid, one of Ken's home town crews had been sent to the same area to cope with a departmental store as it started to burn. They told him, 'We stood by helpless and impatient as there was a shortage of water. We couldn't stop it spreading, and the whole building went up.' Six weeks later when Ken was in Southampton again, wisps of smoke were still rising from its basement.

Another crew in the High Street were trying to create a fire-break by attacking the flames from behind. To do it they had to break in through a shop window. High pressure jets, strangely, would not smash the plate glass, and the heat did not affect it either!

The patrol officer in charge said, 'Throw a brick through it!' A policeman close by heard him. 'Did you say throw a brick through it?' nodding towards the big pane. The flames were reflecting back from it in defiance amidst the endless scream and whooshing of bombs.

'I am afraid so, its the only thing to do,' realising the Law was involved. 'All right, I'll do it for you!' Calmly amid all the drama, the policeman selected a nice large brick and hurled it through the plate glass. Grinning all over his face, he rubbed his hands together, 'Ever since I was so high (and he moved his hand to indicate when he was a boy) I have wanted to smash a shop window with a brick – and now I've done it.' Off he went regardless of the bombs or the fires.

There was a strange feeling in Above Bar that night. Buildings were collapsing and blazing all around Ken. 'The very shops where we were walking round and buying things this afternoon,' he mused to himself. It struck him as so futile, 'What can any man hope to gain by this?'

As the drone continued overhead, more buildings burned and collapsed. During this holocaust two fire stations suffered direct hits, bang went all the spit and polish of a few hours earlier.

For Ken, and the others one unforgettable sight in the middle of the night was a church burning furiously. The steeple was acting as a giant flue and the hot air, as it rushed endlessly upwards, was causing the bells to toll in a most weird fashion.

Occasionally Ken spotted fresh crews he knew, who had answered the Regional call. They were fed as they arrived and then sent straight on to reinforce the battered crews who were still valiantly fighting their losing battle against the flames, but not giving in.

Fresh men enabled water relays to be set up. Long snakes of hoses crossed the city bringing desperately needed water, flowing to the pumps. 'Firemen are worse off than soldiers without bullets,' he grunted to a fellow officer as they got another relay going. 'The soldier can take cover, the fireman has to stand up in the full glare of the fire, he daren't leave in case the water suddenly comes through. And all the time the flames are the targets for the bombs.'

It was 10.30 on Saturday night that a large high explosive bomb hit the Civic Centre. Communications were all cut. Despatch riders immediately began a human life-line taking vital messages to Winchester, there they were transmitted on to Regional headquarters. Firemen might belong to a motley of differing fire brigades but, thank God, the Government's Home Office had set up control centres across the whole country, to draw together the efforts to fight back.

Telephonists at the central fire station could not operate. Southampton's messengers became essential links more than ever before. The women telephonists did not hesitate, they set too cutting huge quantities of sandwiches in readiness for the canteen vans which would be needed to go out to feed the fire-fighters.

* * *

There was a hell of a row when an AFS crew returned to Slough from Southampton, shattered from yet another mad race to aid a blitzed town. It had been another never-to-be-forgotten experience. Yet, here was a 'brass hat' officer bellowing because they had lost a one inch branch and a valve key!

When the men left their station originally – independently as most still did – utmost in their minds was not the dangers they would be facing but the fear of losing any equipment. 'You are going to Southampton,' he told Sam, the leading fireman. 'I have had seven crews go so far and they have all come back losing equipment. I suppose you will be just the same.' Then he added, not 'Good luck' but 'I'll see you when you come back!'

The roads leading to Southampton's central fire station, in Mackenzie Street, were a shambles when Sam arrived. Shops were in tatters, remnants of trams were hanging all over the place, not a soul was to be seen. It was severely blitzed. Lining the fire station's street were taxis, cars, and lorries, all with ladders strapped on them, and the vital grey fire pumps hitched behind. These were the messengers of mercy, in a city which seemed so silent now that the bombers had gone away.

But it wasn't. There was a lot of work waiting for willing hands to do. As the Slough men pulled up, Sam went to report. Immediately his crew were sent to reinforce men already fighting a major fire at a flour mill. They worked on, never complaining, through the night, the next day and all the following night. 'That flour fire is going to last about a week,' Sam told his men. They had not won, but they had done all that was humanely possible.

Remembering the veiled threat, from amid the confusion Sam collected together their gear with great care. Back to the central fire station to report. 'Right, next job is . . . ,' said the controlling officer. Shocked, Sam replied, 'Look sir, these chaps are asleep on the machine, I can't do any more.' There was no argument, 'All right, find the hostel. I have another crew who can take over your machine.'

'Oh no! You're not taking my brigade's pump,' he blurted out. 'I'm sorry it is the Chief Officer's orders, you have no say in the matter,' testily replied the officer.

Next morning, Sam found the leading fireman who had taken it over, with his crew. They were settling down for a rest. 'The car's outside but the pump is down at the dockyards. It's been pumping all night.' Sam's men found the car and headed for the docks. Recovering the pump, they checked their gear. Plenty was missing. Not stolen but left, almost certainly in use, in the heat of the battle.

Sam's good nature was gone, he knew what to expect when he got home. Determinedly, he drove back to Southampton's control. 'Can I see the Chief Officer?' he asked, and was shown in. 'Sir, I am missing . . .' and he listed the items.

'I lost about ten pumps last night, six chaps killed, and you come in here and tell me you have lost some equipment! There was a pause, 'You want to hear what my officer will say . . . ,' Sam was interrupted, 'Get out!'

Returning to the dockyards, Sam and his men searched the other fire units there. They went along pinching everything they needed – but they forgot the nozzle and a key.

When the crew, filthy and tired, drew into Slough, Sam was kept waiting an hour. 'What are you missing?' were the first words of welcome. Told the answer, the officer replied, 'There you are, just as I thought. Once you leave here, you go away and enjoy yourselves.'

Sam told his men, 'He couldn't care less about Southampton. We do, and the next time we go away they can pinch the lot. I don't care about his bloody equipment any more. He should go and see for himself.'

He was still remembering stopping at a pub for a cool beer on the way home. A Navy officer insisted on buying the round. 'We owe you a great debt,' he said. 'We have means of hitting back, you have to stand there and take it.'

*   *   *

Then the German bombers struck at London again. Water for the fire pumps kept failing, so many mains were fractured, as Gordon Castle was to find out. 'I well remember that call. It was the night the City was on fire, and the Guildhall was burnt out,' said Gordon when he came back. 'Where do we start?' was again the question which was uppermost in his mind.

'It was desperate; it seemed uncontrollable – it lasted 48 hours!' St Paul's had stood silhouetted, there were firemen ready to kick off, or put out, incendiaries which struck. It was to be saved from the enemy.

79

Yet, like Ken, he caught his breath as London women still came to help. They walked right down to the pumps with jugs of tea and sandwiches. He remembered whispering to his crew, 'They don't seem a bit scared of the fires.' Somehow it made them feel safer in such an unreal, and, unrecognisable world.

*   *   *

Christmas! 'Jerry's taking a rest, celebrating?' said John. 'If I say it loud he will turn up!' Ken laughed, 'It has been a full calendar. Just think, a year ago, in the midst of all our moving the action station, we were bemoaning what had happened in 1939. Nothing like 1940.'

John laughed back. 'Yes, we were on about the first war budget, Income Tax up to 7s 6d in the pound. Cigarettes and beer up, 1d on a pint. Rationing started, all shop prices were controlled. Every newspaper had to be ordered, there was no spare newsprint to waste copies.'

'And, the Royal Oak was torpedoed and 700 lost,' added Ken, sadly.

'What about this year? The rationing is getting tougher,' responded John. 'Yes, and so is the war,' said Ken, ending the depressing thoughts. It was a cold bleak winter in their minds, as well as outside. But the Luftwaffe did stay away. So did the men who had gone to the Midlands.

*   *   *

Just after Boxing Day they were back, attacking London. The Thames was right out, it was a very low tide, and mud was everywhere. 'No water' was the cry often to be heard. Calls went out to many brigades asking for reinforcements.

Six-inch steel pipes transported by lorries, and clamped together on top of the debris, provided new lifelines. Another inspired innovation it was like gold to those facing the heat without water, it was worth its weight in metal.

Warnings started regularly up to six a night in early January. The war certainly was not over for the AFS.

The thirteenth, and Caversham were also off to Exeter. Ken was chatting to a police inspector. 'We shall be back again visiting you, I'm sure,' said Ken. 'No, the ships in our little harbour put up such a fight, they won't come again.' Such optimism. Ken was looking for him when they returned the next time.

12 · Frozen to the bone

'Whose winning, Hitler or us firemen?' Ken Watson put the question to his number two, Patrol Officer John Lander, back at the Caversham action station. Regional calls had by now become an accepted fact at all the stations, indeed across the country. It was becoming a difficult task to pick the crews to go – the men were feeling the strain.

So many towns and cities were reeling from repeated attacks in their turn, and men were away three, four days, even a week and longer. 'Surely no one can deny that these auxiliaries are now seasoned fire-fighters?'

But it was not only the men going to help, it was those holding the fort, always fearful that 'Jerry' might switch his attack to Reading, such an important rail and road junction, the marshalling yards at Tilehurst, the ordnance factory at Burgh-field, and, of course, the aerodromes, particularly Woodley, just on the edge of town. These were just a few of the risks.

A 'Starfish' decoy site – valuable at blitz cities, to attract the Luftwaffe away from a real target – was ready at Pangbourne, to be set alight to confuse and divert bomb aimers if the town was heavily attacked.

Too often the day crews would have just left the station on their way home, when the sirens would sound and it was back for the period of the alert, so often all night. If anybody didn't hear the siren and appear, it was certain they were flat out exhausted, the temptation to 'skive' was resisted.

Conditions met on these 'jobs' in strange towns varied enormously. Some clearly did not have the facilities available to others. But, still remembering the kindness in Southampton, Ken went on, 'One or two could spare a little more attention to resting and feeding our men.' But still the men helped Ken solve his problem, they continued to provide the extra men by volunteering to go on Regional call.

'I hope the bastards who thought we were, or the rest of the Civil Defence, were Army dodgers, are sorry now.' 'Not likely, stupid people will still think we are dart throwers,' retorted John.

Travelling conditions remained bad. In the bitter first months of 1941, some firemen were still riding on the backs of open lorries, sometimes 100–200 miles. 'Something has got to be done,' Ken continued the conversation. 'They are frozen to the bone – often they can't even dismount when they get to the blitz, they're so cold and stiff.'

'It's as bad when you go by car,' retorted John. 'They lay or crouch on the equipment, there's no room for humans! You can bet you will find every hard object or sharp corner on a long journey. Hose couplings, hurricane lamps, felling axes, crowbars, saws, even the first aid ...'

Interrupting, Ken said, 'I know, and the men are too conscientious to stop for any length of time on the road, they know their help is desperately needed.'

John was determined to try and have the last word. 'I would rather travel on an open lorry than having that pump gear stuck ...' The telephone beat him. 'Purple alert,' said the voice on the other end. It was starting again. 'So would I,' agreed Ken, 'but there ought to be something better.'

It was only minutes before the sirens broke the still of the night. Those on duty took it all in their stride as they piled into or on their vehicles and went off to the action points. In no time others were running and cycling into the courtyard – far removed from its gayer, romantic, atmosphere of a century earlier – ready to man the other fire pumps.

It was hours later that the All Clear echoed over the dawn chorus, and long after incendiary bombs put them into action. Dropped by one of the incessant stream of raiders flying north over the Thames Valley. Probably badly hurt by one of the night fighters, or ack-ack, thought the firemen – and jolly good job somebody's hitting back.

Sitting down, drinking a cup of tea when all was peaceful again, John returned to the nagging topic. 'Do you realise, that people are never going to realise, or understand all we put up with. It will be just like the First World War. In 50 years time, they will not believe it possible.

'Just think what our men, and others just like us from towns all over the country, have been through...'

*   *   *

Been through, was a memory which was going to last for a long time with a group of firemen from another Reading station. In turn with many other men, because of the number as well as intensity of the raids, they were on standby at Fareham for a week, ready to go to the aid of Southampton or Portsmouth.

Away from home for yet another stint, they did not grumble – even though they slept in the workhouse! The beds were quite comfortable, and, they were fed in the naval barracks of HMS Collingwood. The food was good, considering the really bleak time of rationing.

This special night they had to switch to the Methodist Church. All had blankets but no mattresses, but it did not matter. Shorty, from Tilehurst, like the others could lie down and sleep anywhere, all were so tired. But it was a disturbed night, men kept stepping over him, stirring him as they stumbled in the dark.

'What the devil's up,' he thought in his stupor. Suddenly his stomach started rumbling and he made a mad dash in pursuit of the others. The sailors had put salt in their tea!

All were heading out into the road to a public toilet, there was nowhere else. One man was so ill he had to be taken to hospital.

Gordon Castle laughed when the story reached him. He had a vivid memory of

Fareham for another reason. That was before the Navy helped feed them. Disorganisation was the problem. He arrived only to find that the reinforcing base did not know his crew were coming.

There was no food. A few loaves were rustled up and some Marmite. That was all and Gordon was angry. He kicked up a row. When he returned he was on the carpet but, this time, authority agreed with him. 'Perhaps,' he thought, later, 'that was why the Navy came to the rescue.'

*   *   *

'What a January night, it must be the coldest of the year,' said Roger Smith. 'A turntable ladder has been abandoned. It was frozen solid.' When his pump reached Bristol, his troubles started. Pumps already working on the steep hill of a main shopping street had spilled water and, when Roger's crew arrived, the hill was a sheet of ice. It was a massive task just reaching the top and was only achieved by the driver swerving left and right to gain enough grip.

Back from Bristol, he relived that long winter's night of fierce fires. 'I nearly cried as we all tried to roll up our hose. We couldn't, it was frozen solid. We had to leave it behind. All our tunics would crack with the ice in them. Do you know not one of us has got a cold through it.'

He could not forget, the girl standing amid the devastation giving out sandwiches and tea. It was Roger's first trip to Bristol and he admired the quiet way she stood there for hours, regardless. 'That was a nasty night,' he said quietly, almost to himself.

He was not to know he would see her again, when it came his turn to go again. There she was in the thick of it – it was Good Friday and this time it was hot cross buns. He told his wife, as he recounted the quiet bravery. 'She didn't wear any uniform. She was stood outside a garage which burst into flames and we went to fight it.'

Ken, too, was still sorry for Bristol, it had suffered a major raid and stories of what had happened were gradually creeping out. Everybody knew about Coventry but not Bristol? The docks were beneath some of the heaviest bombs; factories were hit, so was the city's historic centre. The Old Market was lost – the fires were out of control. Crews of AFS, including Tilehurst, had been on the road again, but not Ken or his men. Somehow not being there had been harder.

The central fire station had briefly recorded some men going to Bristol – 'It's as if they don't want to know where we go for blitzes,' said John Lander.

His Christmas spirit had not lasted long, although he had been extremely grateful that it had proved quiet. The cinemas, re-opened after their initial shut-down of entertainment, did good business as people looked for relief from their hard lives, and John was among them.

But, both Ken and John had been infuriated that the IRA tried to spoil even that. An explosion in Marks and Spencers, in London's Oxford Street, in the shopping run-up, was followed by two cigarette packet fire bombs in Birmingham cinemas.

83

Ken's convoy was halted one night between Fareham and Gosport, as they endeavoured to move in and help. A nest of incendiaries were blazing right across the road denying them passage. Searchlights were trying to pick out the land mines coming down, so people should know where they would drop.

Then, with hardly a sound, down came the high explosives. One crew, just in front of Ken, were unlucky. Caught in the blast, two men died and three were found seriously injured.

Yet, when the raiders had gone, after a blistering and devastating attack, Ken realised that those unfortunate men were the only casualties from their area that night. Such were the dangers that he quietly whispered to himself, 'God must surely have looked after us tonight.' He looked around and added, 'Thank you.'

He was also recalling his previous visit. That was also dreadful. To get water to fight the fires, the men pumped from the sea for 24-hours at a stretch, in the biting cold. Sailors helped them haul their pumps up the shingle as the tide came in, and back down again as it went out! Their only sleep was a few hours on the end of the jetties in sodden clothes.

It also reminded him of the Portsdown woman, a cook in the fire brigade, who stood watching the blitz, crying because the guns had gone silent. They were out of ammunition, and could not hit back.

*   *   *

'Did you ever sleep in the cells at the clink in Fareham?' Casually the fireman asked his mate as they played a hose into the endless flames. 'No,' said his mate. 'There wasn't an inch of floor space in the Wesleyan Chapel, upstairs or down, so we went and put ourselves in the cells,' chatted on his friend. 'Did you try the church hall?' he asked.

*   *   *

Men still froze without overcoats at these early blitzes, as they did when on duty at home, during that blistering cold winter. Few were yet issued: Gordon Castle looked with envy as the fires he was fighting lit up the Royal Naval tailor's work place in Gosport. Water was pouring over 'lovely, warm, thick overcoats,' and all he could do was look and wish. Such was the honesty of the fire-fighters. Many, of course, being part-timers and losing pay by fighting fires.

So there was anger when a fireman was accused of stealing £66 during a blitz in Portsmouth. When Gordon heard of it he could not believe it, although not one of his men, he knew him quite well. Without wasting any time for niceties, he went and found the fireman. 'Yes, he had handled the money but had given it to a policeman,' he said.

Ken talked with the people still picking at the debris. 'I saw him give the money to a copper,' said an old man. All policemen had regular beats, so it did not take long to find the culprit. After that the word spread among the AFS, 'Make sure you get a receipt for everything.'

*   *   *

Next call for the Caversham men was Plymouth. Dirty night, black-out regulations ensuring that nothing helpful could be seen, and, of course, every road direction sign taken away because of the continued fear of imminent invasion. Broadcasts from Germany had given it renewed threat.

The instructions had been, 'Get to Exeter, fill up with petrol there.' He had, but no food for the men. On they rolled. The open backed Packard had been replaced with an Austin 10, thank goodness in this weather, even if the driver kept crashing the close ratio gearbox.

Ken Watson was lost. Spotting a cottage, he stopped. 'Are we right for Plymouth, please?' he asked the anonymous head that popped out of the opened window. 'I'm not giving you any information,' and bang went the window! He could sense the spirit of defiance.

On the way home he was lost again. 'The telegraph poles', he suddenly said. 'I remember the crossbars are bolted on the side towards London. Keep watching the poles.' As they came over Salisbury Plain Ken was asleep as he drove. They changed his message, 'Keep awake, guv'nor, keep awake.'

Back home, he was glad to find that the Germans were feeling the pressure as well. The raids were easing off – but not ending.

*   *   *

Late at night a mobilising exercise in the big yard of the Reading station drew together another odd collection of vehicles. Once again the cry went up, 'Shorty, give us a hand, our lights have gone.' The AFS electrician, came with screwdriver in one hand and roll of insulating tape in the other.

It was basic work, what little light allowed was much needed. Regular care was given to the oil lamps fixed to the rear of the pumps, there were no electrics in that emergency specification. But, a light on the vehicle was necessary – with the usual proviso, if possible!

This was all new to Harold Randle. 'The grapevine says the Home Office has realised how daft this is and is mass producing towing vehicles, and a lot of them,' Roger told him. 'I hope it's right.'

Apart from the mechanical problems, the exercise worked well. Many others were to follow. When there was time.

First though was answering those staccato messages. 'Eastern, Tilehurst and South, send reinforcing heavy pumps to Fareham.' The South Coast was in more trouble. Earlier three firemen had taken an escape unit to Portsmouth, the calls for major equipment were growing.

85

Still biting winter weather, Reading was given a warming up when incendiary bombs dropped on the 'home' patch at tea-time. It was still nothing like the attention focussed on other towns, particularly Bristol, Portsmouth and London.

Tom came hurrying into Ken's office. Clearly there was more woe from London to be passed on. 'They've hit The Bank underground station and over a 100 people have been killed. A bomb went straight through the road and exploded in the booking hall.' They sat and looked at each other, there was nothing left to be said.

Battling against endless horrors was beginning to pull the local brigades closer together; the men of the AFS had dovetailed in easily with the smaller 'public subscription' brigades from the beginning, well they were almost all volunteers in any case, it was now happening in bigger towns like Reading.

Early AFS volunteers with their newly acquired Worthington Simpson light trailer pump. Thousands were manufactured

Wartime pump-escape with trailer pump, despatch rider, and trusty ATV, taking part in crowd-drawing display.

Wednesday, February 10, 1943, devastation outside St Laurence's Church, Reading. Author is seen with the pump on the mobile dam lorry.

The new turntable-ladder helps make buildings safe during the clearing up operation. The church pinnacles had to be removed. A large framed copy hangs in the reception at the headquarters of the Royal Berkshire Fire & Rescue Service

Early days: Chief Officer E F Batchford, of the Reading Fire Brigade, with members of the AFS, including Jeff Robson to whom this book is dedicated.

At the finale: NFS headquarters staff of A-Division of Fire Force 15, at The Mansion House, Prospect Park, Reading. Centre is Mr Batchford, divisional officer.

Firewomen at A-Division headquarters were well-known for their charming as well as impressive physical training display team.

Civil Defence services combined to present a pageant on the stage of the Palace Theatre, in aid of the Red Cross, in 1943. Photo, Berkshire Chronicle

Getting ready for war: the first trailer pumps, one hitched to an open lorry, with action station being protected by sandbags at Balmore Estate, Caversham. In contrast below . . .

A Reading firewoman logs mobilising information in the control room of Fire Force 15 headquarters at Taplow.

13 · Before the war

Harold Randle swung open the picket door in the sliding garage entrance and pushed his cycle through. He was glad to be in the dry, however bare conditions were in the Oxford Road station. Rain was dripping off his steel helmet, his service gasmask case seemed sturdy enough not to have let the water in, and, thank goodness, those waterproof cycling coat and leggings were wonderful. 'And I haven't got wet feet, like I did in the LDV, with these wellies,' he thought to himself.

'You picked the wrong time to be out,' said Roger Smith, the leading fireman, seeing the youngster. 'I had to take some documents down to The Butts fire station. I got there in the dry,' replied Harold. 'What a place that is. It really is basic.'

When Harold had taken off the wet gear, Roger pushed a cup of hot tea into his hand. 'Come and get round the stove.' The message was quite fatherly, although Roger was not going to say that he realised Harold was well below the age to volunteer.

'Hadn't you been to the Butts before?' Harold shook his head as he drank. 'That was the town-fathers only fire station until war broke out. Tell him about it, Jim,' he said to the other chap sat by the stove.

'It was small with a corrugated tin roof,' chuckled Jim. 'The old brigade was ill-equipped to look after the town. What was the size in those days?' In 1938–39 Reading borough must have been bordering on 100,000 people, he explained. 'We weren't equipped for the job. Our only washing facilities was one of those old shallow sinks out the back; one of those stone sinks, in a shed affair, must have been a stable, across a yard. We had no water unless we heated it up in a bucket on a stove like this. Nowhere to dry your clothes either, if you were soaked at a fire.'

Roger laughed, 'Go on, you'll make us believe you were a regular brass hat. No, he was one of the few part-time retained firemen,' he added to Harold. 'Well the poor devils did have a hard time,' said Jim. 'There were just eight brass hats, and 12 or 14 of us retained men. We used to get two shillings for a drill. Let me tell you some more.'

As Jim got into his stride, Roger listened as well. Jim drew quite a picture of the old station. It housed three appliances. There was one small tender, an old Dennis – 'DP 2000,' he added with nostalgia – it had a pump and carried an extension ladder, which used to be the first turn out. There were also two pump escapes.

'One was extremely old, which must have dated back to the early 1900s,' he said exaggerating. 'It originally had solid tyres!' Jim rattled off, DP 741 – he paused,

'Actually it was built in 1912, Reading bought two of them. They were their first motorised fire engines.

'To get them in the station was a tight fit, and to get that one back into its corner was a work of art.' Jim explained how that old Dennis only came out when the brigade had a real job on its hands.

'The men were on continuous duty, working three shifts. The thing that got me was that at night there were only two on duty, in the day there were probably five. Mind you they had to take turns to cycle home to eat their dinner, so they were often short-handed.

'At night it didn't matter what came in, that first tender had to get away with those two blokes.' Dramatic stuff. However it was clear that was going to be the end of what was a long conversation from Jim, 'How about you going over to the fish and chip shop? They haven't any fish or sausages, but bring back some chips.'

But, Harold already had that journalist's instinct and his look showed he wanted to know more. 'Talk to Henry Barnes, at Caversham Road, the new main station, he'll tell you some good stories.'

It was another special big Sunday exercise soon after when Harold found himself at the central station. He had been pedalling backwards and forwards through the back streets of the town with messages because the telephones lines were described as 'blown up!' – and the main roads were said to be impassable.

Already he had found his guts tightening up when, near his home station, an umpire lit a mock bomb and somebody screamed 'Gas'. His helmet was tilted back and head inside his service respirator in record time. Harold was very conscious of gas; his father had been wounded and taken prisoner when the Huns used it in the First World War. Dad always called them Huns. The first pages of Dad's Home Guard notebook carefully recorded details of the gas lectures – he hadn't forgotten.

The cover said, No 2 Platoon, Z146 MT Coy, Home Guard. Inside, it began: Gas. 3 states – solids, liquids, gas or vapour; 4 groups – harassing, lethal, toxic, vesicant; 2 kinds – persistent, non persistent.

Overleaf it listed in painful detail what these gases could do to the body, especially the inside! Phosgene, chlorine, arsenic, and mustard – the heavy, dirty, oily liquid which frightened everyone with its fear of terrible attacks on the skin. 'Smells like garlic ... causes a hollow centre blister like a tomato. Blister must not be pricked,' he had written in his perfect handwriting.

This time, however, the shout was not even for test. The smoke and smell from the 'bomb' had made a fireman nervous, and he screamed 'Gas'. These exercises were very realistic.

Back at the main station, 'Stand easy' had been called, and Harold spotted Henry enjoying his much-earned cup of tea, and sidled up. 'Hello kid,' he said, 'The new uniform looks smart.' 'Thanks. I have been hearing about the pre-war regular fire brigade. Can you tell me more?'

Henry laughed, he waved his hand towards the collection of old cars and lorries parked in the yard, everything from the crash-gearbox taxis, to the posh Buicks and Packards, all hugging their own trailer pumps, and said, 'Well it wasn't anything like this.'

'At night there would be two of us. It did not matter what call for help came, you had to go with just those two blokes. First, we had to ring the bells at the homes of the other full-time men to call them out, on an old hand generator. Then we had to phone the police and water turncock men. You couldn't even put your gear on because the other bloke had started up the appliance while that was being done, and he was ready to go.'

He warmed to his memories. 'We had terrible battles with fires at night. It was a devil, you were on your knees before any help could arrive. I remember the paint works in Minster Street. I didn't get my boots on until the second appliance arrived! It always took them at least six to nine minutes.'

Harold could see in his mind this immense store of volatile materials, all certain to burn or explode, blazing in the middle of the town centre. Two men scrambling alone to fix standpipes at the nearest hydrants and then each running out a line of hose, to put water on the fire. 'Fortunately there was a good pressure of water,' mused Henry.

'To think there is still a problem to find enough men who can drive,' he said looking again at the odd collection of vehicles. 'I could drive a car when I joined in '37 but I remember there was very little tuition. One of the first nights it was my turn on duty, I got landed. I was very raw then. You were supposed to put your head down and get some sleep but I couldn't I was too worried.

'I didn't know where half the flaming roads were, there was no street index. We had a Corporation book telling us where to find the hydrants.

'We had a shout to a fish and chip shop in Orts Road. It was the first time I had ever driven to a fire, the other bloke with me couldn't drive. The bloody thing, I was on the wrong side going up King's Road and I thought, 'I hope the lights and everything are for me because I daren't stop!'.

'It was really terrible and this was the light tender, with a sloping back. It only carried an extension ladder and a pump. We didn't have much in the way of drills in those days.'

Henry laughed as he said, 'The fire was the easy bit. It was good to get on the side seats and have a ride back, and not drive.'

'One of the biggest fires I ever fought was the County Theatre, in Friar Street – one of the town's main roads – in 1937. That was a hell of a fire. You can imagine we had to get the three appliances out for that, the old boy had to come out of the corner.

'I was on DP 741 with the sub-engineer. There were just two, again, at first. When we arrived we got to work in Broad Street. We raised the old escape and took hose across the roof of Bulls' departmental stores to get at it.'

Looking still at all the different fire pumps, from numerous stations, massed in the yard, Henry said thoughtfully, 'There was no assistance between one brigade and another. Call in anybody else, like Sonning or Pangbourne? Not likely, they just didn't want interference. I remember how the machine from Wokingham RDC used to come through Reading to get to Spencers Wood on the other side!'

'What happened at the theatre?' asked Harold. 'The County was a colossal job. It was through the roof when we got there. If you can imagine two people trying to struggle with that. They knew other people would come as soon as they could but the time factor was quite considerable. Everybody turned out on those occasions, and the two turncock men from the water company, used to come and divert the water supplies to give us pressure.

'As I say, nobody came from outside. I remember one fellow fractured his ankle and they carried him from the top of the escape and sat him on a high wall with a hose – they couldn't afford for him to go off to hospital.

'That was the state of things, we were really hard pressed.' Waving his cup, he said, 'There was no question of refreshments or anything like that. It was hard going.'

Full-time firemen received £3 a week, he recalled. 'Not bad before the war.' All were tradesmen, mechanics, blacksmiths, whatever, so that they could carry out jobs to keep the engines and station going.' When he joined, he said, he was the exception, because there was so much paper work – 'Perhaps some people did realise there was much to be done in case of a war?'

Retained men used to get two shillings for a drill; half-a-crown for a turnout, and two shillings for every hour after that, he said. The retaining fee was a few pounds. Full-time men were on continuous duty.

'We got a day off a week and, if you went to the pictures, they would put a notice up on the screen telling you there was a fire. If you were caught in your best suit, you'd had it, with no leggings provided you could write your suit off!'

'Mind you, you didn't normally even get your boots on when you were on duty' – he was still thinking of fighting that paint fire in his socks! 'You were standing on the back of the appliance with your tunic, and everything else, over your arm. You tried to dress without being thrown off, quite often somebody's boots would fly.'

'We had a fight over those leggings, the fire chief was real anti, he thought it was soft. We used to get absolutely soaked.'

'The fire chief was a mad devil,' he said, with a degree of pride. He used to ride around on a motorbike and side-car originally. 'I used to ride in that flaming sidecar, oh dear, that was hell.' He used to be a sailmaker in the Royal Navy, he had a load of ribbons from the First World War, and he would grab the chance to drive the big escape whenever he could.

'Although he was in charge, he was really the second officer. The real man in control was the Chief Constable. He was a sight when he came round, he was a real disciplinarian.'

It was November, 1939, when the Reading Brigade moved to Caversham Road. That was after it got the new pump escape, ARD 780. 'I believe the station was built because the town was being pressed by the new Fire Services Act; I think people realised just how antiquated we were.

'I have never forgotten the firemen's relief when we moved to Caversham Road. We thought we were in clover. Now look at us!'

They could well have been the words of Ken Watson as he set off again for the West Country.

*   *   *

90

The nightly trek to the hills at Plymouth began with almost clockwork regularity. People from many of the towns from which Ken and his fellow firemen came could never conceive the horror these people were going through.

Ken watched as mothers dragged children along, because they had no transport, while cars with one or two people went by without deigning to give a lift. A small thing but it puzzled him as one of the hundred who came hundreds of miles to help!

When the families got away, pantechnicons were used as sleeping quarters for children. 'Hungry, frightened children,' as he described them to Lucy, when he was back home and was able to 'enjoy' a night in his own bunk-bed in his shelter.

'Dead people, blast damage, fire destruction, chaos in town after town, a common enough sight to those who endure it, but meaningless to others in dozens of towns like Reading.'

He told her, 'It's worth what we are doing. All the fire services, indeed all the Civil Defence men and women, are fighting back. We're not going to let the Luftwaffe smash this country to our knees.

'I'll tell you what, I would like to get hold of one of those women who were sending me the white feathers and take her with me on the next blitz call.'

Ken was still feeling emotional, and humbled, by the way he and his men had been treated in a small Devon village on their way back from Plymouth. His men had been working practically non-stop for three days and nights in the city and were worn-out.

The Devonport seaplane base had copped it again, its oil tanks set alight. Firemen kept going, making intense efforts to douse fires before the next night, so that the Luftwaffe should not have ready-made direction beacons. 'Knackered' was his word for it. Told they could go home, they set off.

They were all mentally and physically sick. The school where they were stationed was fired with incendiaries, but that seemed nothing compared with the next moment. The firemen in a crew, detailed to be the one to go out into the blitz before Ken's, had only just left the school when they were hit by a land mine, and never seen again.

As they drove into Chudleigh, Ken said 'Stop.' It was obvious they needed a break. Ken went up to the door of a house at random and asked, 'Is there anywhere my firemen could get any food?' Not an easy question, in 1941 when food supplies were desperately short, and rationing at its tightest.

The firemen's weary looks, drawn pale faces and red rimmed eyes, said everything. The fact that they stank of smoke, and probably worse, was enough to have put off many who might have answered such a door knocking. But not this night.

It turned out to be the vicarage and the vicar, without hesitation, led them to the church hall. The Devonshire folk moved into action.

The Home Guard brought palliases; the village pub landlord appeared with the largest jar of pickled onions that Ken had ever seen. Next came bread and cheese, and glasses of beer. It was a feast and, when it was over, the men had their first sleep for five nights. The Home Guard promised to mount a guard over their vehicles all night.

In the morning, the firemen were roused and Ken was able to say his thanks, and take his men home in daylight. That village understood what its nearby cities, and neighbours, were suffering. They could see the flames and feel the pain.

*   *   *

Harold Randle was telling Roger Smith – in charge of one of the Tilehurst station's crews on the widespread Sunday 'blitz' exercise – what he had been learning of the pre-war Reading brigade. 'It was a colossal job for them moving to the new headquarters at the same time as the town was commandeering all the action station premises,' said Roger. 'Henry Barnes, was going round the clock, trying to cope with the paperwork.

'Especially when the equipment, the pumps, ladders, hose and all that, started to arrive. You know that was done through the Government.'

Although many of the units had moved out again on the exercise, Roger's 'new' Studebaker was standing waiting to be sent to an 'incident'. The engine was turned off, to save petrol, but the driver's hand was self-consciously not far from the starter. The 'buzz' was that Huntley and Palmers' big biscuit factory was the centre of the action.

'As emergency pumps and hose arrived they were parked wherever they could be put, but, soon the action stations were coming through. Deliveries were then made straight to them to keep in store,' Roger explained.

'When one of the first pumps came, the fire chief was giving instruction to some of the AFS. One lad was 6 ft 7 in tall, and it was one of the little Worthington Simpson's. I remember the chief saying 'Pull out the choke' – and he did, the whole cable came out in his hand!'

The two firemen and Harold in the back of the car laughed, and wriggled themselves a little less uncomfortable on top of the standpipes, ropes, axes, and other gear which wouldn't fit on the heavy pump trailed behind. On the roof was the 30-foot extension ladder and other essential gear. All held in place by a home-made gantry.

Alf, the part-timer driver, was daily used to the famous box-like Trojan tea vans, used by Brooke Bond, with the lever in the cab pulled to turn the flywheel and start the engine. But he had got the hang of the powerful, although top heavy and overloaded, saloon. Harold was just wondering who had owned it in the days before petrol rationing? It must have been someone's pride and joy. Then the orders came.

'Huntley and Palmers,' said Roger, jumping in beside the driver. 'Go down by the railway station and round beside the prison.' The American car responded and, moving fast, she heeled heavily as she met the changed camber of the main road. The only traffic about was ARP and a heavy rescue unit, so there was nothing in the way as the car charged off.

There was plenty of activity in The Forbury, beside the prison, with men and women rushing about taking their part in the exercise. The Studebaker was really travelling when, suddenly, Roger shouted, 'Watch out!' In the same instance the

92

driver had seen the lines of charged hose crossing the road ahead. Wooden ramps, to make it possible to cross safely when travelling gently, were protecting them.

Alf hit his brakes hard, for a second the car seemed to be stopping quickly; then the pump, weighing nearly a ton, thumped its backside! The car took off, hit the ramps and projected itself skywards. Crashing down again it careered along the road, rocking from side to side, with the immensity of a pendulum in a grandfather clock.

There was a feeling that time was standing still – as with all horrors of the blitzes – it seemed certain the car was going over. The pump, pushing and pulling, as its own manual brake caught and let go, seemed determined to wreck their chances. But, slowly, the violent motion eased and the car came back to earth. 'God, that was worse than being attacked by Jerry,' gasped Roger, as his driver stopped.

Recovered, they set off again and were signalled on to the bridge which crosses the Holy Brook. 'We have to set our pump up here and run a relay, imagine the whole factory's on fire,' he gasped as he came back with his instructions. 'I think the Home Office inspectorate are running this. They certainly are putting the heat on.'

Four men were handling the pump which normally rated a crew of five. Harold was making up the number – he remembered the early advice from Len Hall, 'You're a fireman first, messenger second, in the AFS.'

'Come on young Harold, let's see if you really are a good pump man. This bridge is a tough test to raise water, it's reckoned to be the maximum lift possible. Get the pump started, check the screw joints on the hose, tie a rope from the pump to the basket when you throw it in.'

Harold gave a visible grunt as he made sure no air could creep into the joints of the long armoured suction, threw the wrenches into the locker, expertly slipped a clove-hitch round the suction, and boy-handled it through the railings down into the water. Opening up the throttle, he pressed down the priming lever and watched the vacuum dial lift. 'Come on, come on,' he urged himself, then suddenly there was water coming up. Waving an arm to Roger, he spun open the valve to let water pass out along the line of hose and steadied the throttle. It was a proud moment, he could hold his place – as he was to learn many times.

Huntley & Palmers' own firemen were at work on the same exercise. Most of the action seemed to be in Gas Works Road, so probably other men were busy showing their skill at coping with strafed gasometers? thought Harold. Roger came back, 'You're doing well.' That was a compliment.

He talked as he stood watching. 'Did you know that H & Ps made headline news, used to have their own fireboat, showed it off to the Maharajah of Nepal in 1908? Very modern it was, water jet propulsion and a monitor to throw water for the fire fighting. Bet they wish it was still around now.'

'Are there many other private fire brigades in town?' asked Harold. Roger nodded and listed some: Co-op Printing Works, Pulsometer Engineering, Co-op Bakery, Elliotts the woodworkers, Woodley Aerodrome, and the Burghfield Ordnance Factory, quickly came to his mind. 'We all work together now, we help with their training. That includes Brock Barracks, the Royal Berkshires' depot, that's a special liaison for Tilehurst.

'Heelas, the departmental store, they have a brigade. Our own patrol officer came from them. They all have night crews, like firewatchers in other factories and offices.

'Different from the old days. Mind you some of the town brigades around are still pretty difficult, although much less so. They are all chief officers within their own rights.'

He waved as the limousine engine of Sonning drove by. 'They're a good crowd, not long back from Bristol. Wokingham and Pangbourne were there at the same time.

'Pangbourne, Lambourn and Henley, have just been down to Bath. I think they went on to Avonmouth, certainly Lambourn did. I cannot keep count of all the calls.'

Roger took over the controls, 'Go and have a look at what's happening. Follow the relay. You might see our fire boat, it's normally on the Kennet by the brewery, but I think it has been brought down.'

'Fire boat? I didn't know Reading had one,' questioned Harold. 'Yes, the chief officer, and a couple of the regulars, with a Thames Conservancy pilot, fetched it from Oxford early in the war. Go and find it.'

*   *   *

Many buildings were being saved from incendiaries by stirrup pump parties, not just houses, but churches and factories, as people began taking their turn as fire watchers. All the station officers were urged by the chief officer to go and give talks and demonstrations.

'Pop up to Reading University,' he said one day to Gordon Castle. 'Give them a talk, and take some men and give a demonstration. Use some of the American incendiary bombs we have to let off.'

When Gordon walked on to the stage in the Great Hall and the curtains were pulled there were 400 people! He nearly fell through the floor. But the seat of learning was very keen to do just that. Soon they were all outside practising.

As the training was progressing in Caversham, Ken Watson hit on a simple way of giving it realism. Emptying all their gear from one of the coach-house garages, they piled rubbish inside, set it alight, then pulled shut the doors. When the smoke crept through the cracks, a door was opened and the stirrup pumpers sent in! On their bellies they crawled around the walls until able to direct their jets of water to douse the fire. 'The girls are best,' said Ken, and that was an admission from him.

Other AFS men were also singing the praises of the latest, men and women fire-fighters.

The Southern station found out when they answered a Saturday morning call to a house fire in the old part of town. As they drove up Bill Coker, the leading fireman, could see a street party, women and men, with their stirrup pump, in action.'There is another pump at the back of the house,' shouted the street leader.

'Length of hose to a hydrant but don't turn it on,' said Bill to his men. He went to look. Through a slot where they had raised the sash window one team were aiming accurately at the flames engulfing the front room. At the back the others were squirting down the full length of the passage. It was soon under control without the 'interference' of the AFS.

Reporting back, Bill telephoned the central station, 'Extinguished by street fire fighters!' The chief officer would not believe it and went to see for himself.

*   *   *

There were some who were just as perplexed after a early morning fire at a Wrens' training school at Windsor. That was important to the war effort and the firemen turned out at speed, and in numbers. The sight that met them as they arrived was the main topic for weeks.

The girl sailors had surrounded the blazing room with 30 stirrup pumps and as some pumped and others aimed the tiny jets, the rest were non-stop refilling the buckets of water. Nobody let up until the fire was out.

It was an incredible lesson of what could be achieved. The firemen had never seen 30 in action together and their own equipment was not needed. 'The stirrup pump is what should be given the George Cross,' grunted one amazed fireman. 'And you can buy one for just 24s 6d!'

14 · 'Never ending'

Disastrous night bombing raids returned across Britain as 1941 moved towards Spring, and the weather improved. The war news abroad was still grim. Targets were wide and varied, sometimes a lot of planes, often just a few flying spread out across the country to keep the firemen and Civil Defence alert – well as alert as tired-out men and women could stand the strain. Especially as the tiny 1kg incendiary was causing incredible damage.

'It's amazing how Britain is relying on volunteers. How long can we keep it up?' John Lander grunted, 'How long will these cars and lorries keep us rolling?'

This time he did not have long to wait to learn the answer. The 'buzz' was right that the Home Office had recognised the problem. The decision had been made by Government not to rely on the civic authorities but to treat the desperate situation of transport just like they ordered the city-saving pumps. Two thousand towing vehicles were being produced. They were copying the idea of one go-ahead authority. Powerful enough to pull the pumps, the 'van' bodies, but with no back doors, would provide lockers for the gear and relatively comfortable seats for the crew.

'Hurrah, somebody loves us,' shouted Ken Watson when he heard. 'Now we have to hope the first arrives soon. But until new vans arrived, the load-up and unload of the lorries as they responded was a test of endurance on every siren at every station.

Permanent vehicles changed as they broke down or wore out and, one evening, Harold found one of the miniature 'fire engines', built on the elderly taxi bodies, standing in the first call spot.

He was not staying on duty, it was the turn of another messenger, Bruce. The bells called out the crew. Hanging on the miniature side seats, as it made its best speed, they found themselves careering down a hill on the far side of Tilehurst. It was out of control as the weight of the trailer pump took over. The taxi leapt the pavement on a bend, 'flew past' a sandbagged Home Guard post and crashed into a sand pit. Bruce, and the others, with no protection, were thrown in all directions. 'Thank God,' he said, 'If we had been able to hang on we would have been squashed!'

When he met Harold again the following night, 'Lucky to be able to tell it,' were his words.

*   *   *

Old-fashioned good luck turned up for Roger Smith and his 'oppo'; tough luck for the rest of his crew. 'Plymouth this time, but we have been ordered to Bath for starters.' The word spread among the men next on call. Off they went, never knowing what to expect, blitz calls might all seem the same but there was always the unexpected.

Arriving in Bath, food was laid on. 'That was a slap-up feed,' said Roger. The relaxed pleasure did not last long. In came an officer, 'Leading fireman and driver outside. I want you to proceed with your unit to Plymouth. Leave your other men behind.'

That told a story: during the first night of the raid a lot of equipment had been lost in the city. It was that they needed more than men.

Roger and his driver didn't argue, off they went in the comfort of their Hudson Terraplane, with only two aboard. As they drove into Plymouth, going up a steep hill, the American car broke down. They were within sight of the fire station.

Walking in and reporting to the station officer, Roger told him they had not made it. 'We can make up a crew with these two from Poole,' he offered. 'You will have to repair my unit before it can be used.' They were sent to eat and, again, had a good meal. 'Times are certainly changing,' thought Roger.

Tired, they turned in – and slept undisturbed through a very heavy raid. They were never called to fight fires. The first they knew was a despatch rider in the morning waking them with a message, 'You had better get down to Drake, the naval base, for breakfast.'

Sitting down with food on their plate, Roger spotted his three crew, he had left in Bath, walking in. 'You're as black as the ace of spades. What have you been up to?'

'You rotten so and so's,' they chorused, realising how clean and fresh Roger and his driver looked. 'Soon after you left, they wanted men. They chartered a bus and brought us to Plymouth and we've been fire fighting all night!'

Released to return home, Roger asked, 'What's happened to our car?' The officer replied, 'It went to the tram and bus depot, you will have to go there. 'How do we get there?' 'See the policeman outside.'

Roger did. The policeman as calmly as you like called over a double-decker bus and said, 'Take these men to the depot.' The three tired men climbed the stairs and stretched on the long seats for a brief rest, Roger and his driver sat sedately inside.

An engineer greeted them; he looked just as tired working on in the confusion. 'Well, I have done the best I can, I don't think it will be all that good. It might get you home!' It was a well-meant message, Roger realised that. 'Thanks a million.'

It was not long before a gear change gave trouble. 'Don't you change gear any more,' said Roger, 'I will warn you of the hills.' All the way back to Reading they raced down every slope and charged up the other side, struggling to top the summits – and made it.

'How did you get on,' asked the duty men as they helped push the Terraplane into the action station. 'Plymouth was great,' said Roger, 'full of Cornish pasties.' There were howls from the others.

*   *   *

97

Lady Luck was also with Messenger Harold Randle. Flames from another big blaze of magnesium at Caversham Mill swept high into the sky. Yellow, purple, red with the heat. High enough for John Lander, from Caversham, to say, 'The Jerries can see that in France. I hope they have a night fighter up protecting us.' John was first there, but calls went out to all the stations. He was right, the yellow, purple, and red, warnings came within the hour. 'Poetic, the colours are the same,' he thought aloud.

At that period sirens were keeping everyone awake for most of the night. Three or four times the rising and dipping tone of the warning would sound. At least the devastating initial two minutes note had long since been cut back to one.

This night Harold was on duty at the Oxford Road station. Everybody had turned in at the earliest opportunity to snatch a little rest on the bunks upstairs. No siren had yet breached the night. Clang, clang, clang, the strident rattle broke into everybody's stupor.

Harold stirred, 'What's that the alarm clock?' he slurred. The voice of the little Scot sleeping above him, was excited as he awoke. With practised skill he dropped straight into his boots positioned in readiness. 'Alarm clock be....' and buttoning his leggings to the waist buttons of his trousers – everybody always slept in their clothes – he was gone down the stairs. Even in that broad Scottish brogue it didn't take Harold seconds to realise both what he said, and what he meant. It was a fire call. He rolled into his boots and shot down the stairs.

In that fraction of time he was too late. The firemen were crushing into the sleek, but heavily laden, Studebaker limousine with Jack, the driver, already moving out through the door. Depressed, disgraced Harold felt, he walked over to the control room to tell them he had missed a shout. He was even more miserable when he learnt it was a big one at the magnesium factory.

Waiting for the men to come back seemed the longest hours of his short life. When they did, they had a story to tell. Roger, the leading fireman, and Jack were still clearly shaken.

As they arrived, and were walking towards the fire, there was a mighty explosion. 'The blazing metal blew up into the air, over our heads, and came crashing down behind us! It was literally up our backsides. It was too near. We were lucky!' he added.

Harold stiffened as he listened. A messenger's routine was always to follow the officer-in-charge closely. 'God, if I had been there, I would have copped the lot!' he blurted out. For a moment everyone was strangely quiet, a recognition of the truth. It was the only call he had missed. God certainly seemed to be on his side. Strange that he had just been confirmed (although, of course, he couldn't tell them that!).

*　　*　　*

Another date that Ken was to especially remember was written up in his diary. 'The bombers have had another go at both Benson and Woodley aerodromes; many fires started in Birmingham; well-known buildings in Coventry, which survived a few months earlier, destroyed and 120-plus people killed. Some Reading AFS have gone as far as Manchester. London and the oil tanks at Thameshaven targets yet again.'

As Ken pieced together his fragments of information, he realised that, despite the hits on the Midlands, it was the South Coast that was suffering the greatest damage. Southampton, Bournemouth, Cosham, Poole, and Ryde on the Isle of Wight, all had people dead.

Gas Mask Week, because of the still real worry of poison from the air, had come and gone. Malta and Torbruk were never out of the news. He shook his head.

These raids on the South Coast ports seemed never ending, they had been hit since the first days of the Battle of Britain, as Hitler had prepared for his invasion. 'Were things getting worse?' he asked himself.

Ken was sitting in his tiny office, behind the watchroom, when the phone rang. The message, 'Be ready to take 30 men with full kit to Southampton at 0800 tomorrow, and to stay for an indefinite period.' He went home and told Lucy. She hugged him tight but didn't say a word at first. Then, simply, 'Come on, let's go to bed, you're going to need sleep.'

Next morning he was at the central fire station early, to meet the men from all over the area, and stow the kitbags and fire fighting gear on the bus which was waiting.

It was an uneventful journey but, as they approached the vital port, Ken was amazed at the number of barrage balloons. They seemed to be floating serenely in the air, the fabric glinting and disarmingly peaceful. It was more than he had ever seen at other towns in the front line of the bombers. The hub of chat from the other men showed they had recognised the same thing.

It wasn't long before they all could see the raw unmistakable signs of recent raiding as the bus headed for the fire station. The authorities were clearly aware that the Luftwaffe was turning its attention to the ports.

Reporting to the controlling officer, Ken said, 'I have brought the men from Reading.' 'Thank God, we are pleased to see you. You will replace the casualties we had last night,' was the reply.

'Your billets are in the school next door,' Ken was told as he reported. Kitbags were heaved on to the beds they chose, and they said 'Hello' to AFS from other towns, all there for the same reason.

'Let's go and look round the fire station, get acquainted with the different appliances, all the signs are we are going to be busy,' Ken told his men. 'Be ready to move at 12.30 for dinner,' advised the control room officer. Ken was to remember that, and tell others, because they were taken to a restaurant and given a slap-up dinner, paid for by Southampton Corporation. Not the treatment given by many others towns.

'Why could Southampton do this without any fuss or bother, when our own town failed miserably to provide shelter or food for the hundreds of firemen who came to stand by, and provide fire cover, while we were at the London Docks?' he asked John when he got back home safely.

But a lot was to happen before that debate. In the afternoon the men paraded.

99

Some were despatched to Southampton's action stations but the majority were kept at the main station, including Ken.

There was a short, sharp raid that Friday evening. The fires were easily dealt with without the reinforcements being needed. But, that was a false reprieve, later the bombers came again. Everything seemed alight as Ken and his men were sent to Above Bar – to the very street where the restaurant had served them – and, alas, it was gone! The meals for Ken's men were the last it served.

It was a night to be remembered. Ken had with him some 'brass hats', out of town at last, fighting their first blitz call, with Ken, an AFS officer in charge. Together they were working in a jewellers, standing on diamonds, rings, and other pretty trinkets. A soldier stood sentry with fixed bayonet!

Everyone mucked in next morning for the routine duties. The station floor was scrubbed and hosed down, brass on the equipment cleaned, school room floors scrubbed – firemen everywhere in the country did their best to see that life went on as normal as possible. But the station was to look very different before the night was out.

Equally everything was being done for the reinforcements comfort, but now the main meals meant a quarter-of-a-mile-walk to a canteen.

It was 6 pm when the sirens sounded. Just a few minutes later – flying time was brief from the French airfields – the Heinkel bombers sent down the first flares. Then the shooting began. It seemed to be the task of all the ack-ack gunners to shoot down those flares.

Ken and the other firemen stood gazing up, faces tense and waiting beneath their steel helmets. The whole town was bathed in a sickly yellow glow. Into the sky flew the tracers, definitely aimed at those flares.

Still the illumination floated down and, outside the station and school play-ground, the firemen waited for what they knew was coming. Inside one of the shelters another group were playing cards by the light of torches.

Presently Ken, and the others, heard the familiar whoosh, whoosh, of the canisters of incendiary bombs coming nearer and spilling their cargo. A few seconds later, 'The dammed things are everywhere,' shouted Ken, quite spontaneously. There was no need, everyone knew. Just then, there was a hell of a crash by the shelter, rushing there Ken found a flare case, smelling strongly of calcium, but minus its parachute. 'Probably shot away by the ack-ack,' he thought.

The glow by now was beginning to diffuse the sky and, just behind them, a large fire was seen to be springing up. Flames were high above the roofs of the houses. Then came the crash of the expected high explosive bombs.

It seemed no time before Ken and the others were called inside the station and he felt unhappy as he was designated to detail men to make up the various crews. He knew that the men to move out first were bound to be sent into the thick of it at the Docks. 'I will send the men from my own town, rather than have any suggestion of favouritism,' he thought to himself. It was no time to show his feelings.

Everyone sensed that this raid was going to be heavy, as the fire reports came flooding in. The private houses were left to the stirrup pump teams, crews being despatched to the main areas of fire.

Just around the corner another flare case fell and smashed the pavement. Ken's thoughts turned to sunrise as the glow of the fires were causing the buildings to be silhouetted against the sky. Not a soul was to be seen, apart from Civil Defence workers and their vehicles.

One of the local officers whispered to Ken, 'Another Regional call has gone out! 'From the chatting which suddenly replaced the deadly silence among the few men still to be sent out, it was clear that the news was quickly spreading. 'Small encouragement, it will be at least an hour before any crews could arrive in Southampton,' replied Ken. 'It's up to us to do what we can to hold the fires in check.'

It was not long before the news came back that in parts of the town water supplies were falling short. The sound of the ack-ack guns stopped – ammunition had run out, or couldn't be got to the gunsites. 'Jerry is really having it his own way, he's picking his targets and dropping his eggs just as he likes,' said Ken.

The first fire that had caught his eye, just behind the fire station, proved to be an oil shop, standing on the corner of the road. The three inch diameter incendiary had done its job as the glittering shower of magnesium splinters took hold in such a wealth of combustible material. It was an inferno.

Ken sent the last crew from the station to it, as it seemed to be spreading dangerously. The men found not only several shops and houses on either side involved but several shops opposite. The blaze had jumped the street and fired, by heat radiation, the other shops. These standing on the corner of a side road had, in turn, spread to a public house opposite and the pub had repeated, in its turn, just what the oil shop had done. All from one small bomb of 36 in a canister!

A light trailer pump had been the only appliance left for the crew to take. With this small but prized piece of equipment they had to do their best. It was the same odds facing other firemen at large fires. All were anxiously waiting for the Regional reinforcements. 'We know they are on the road and driving hard, but they cannot arrive yet,' Ken tried to comfort his men.

Many that night learnt how much determined men could achieve with these Home Office pumps. It was sheer hard work around the oil shop that stopped it from spreading further. Then, just as the men were winning their fight, it seemed as if the bomb aimers were attracted by the brilliant glare. More bombs hit the nurses' quarters just behind the public house.

Debris was hurled into the fire which at once spread into what was left of the nurses' quarters. From there it quickly spread on to engulf the hospital. Ken's nightmare battle was just one of the incidents which hundreds of others faced that night. 'People don't realise the appalling conditions facing auxiliary firemen in all these blitzes on our ports and industrial cities,' he told John when he eventually got back to Caversham. But that was much later.

*   *   *

Ken wiped his blackened brow as morning came; suddenly the silence in contrast sounded as loud as the bombs themselves. He realised that the last bomber had

101

turned for France. Inevitably, came the unenviable job of 'damping down', getting as many of the fires as possible to a state that they would not break out again the next night. It was a time to organise as many relief crews as possible, and a break for those who had suffered the worst.

As morning grew, people began to appear heading for their work, undaunted by the beating they had received. Or at least to find out if they had anywhere left to go to work! Girls, as well as men, were tip-toeing over the debris, giving a wave and a smile as they met the damp and dirty firemen.

They could see these men had not stopped for food. 'Would you like a sandwich?' was the almost embarrassed question from one young woman. It was her way of trying to say 'Thank you'. She blushed as the fireman said 'Yes, please.' He recognised the sacrifice in such days of tight rationing but, by God was he hungry. She pushed her packet of sandwiches into his hand and went on, happy even if she was going to be hungry herself.

Others, men as well as women, were quick to follow, not just that day but for many more to come. A lot of early morning breakfasts were only possible by such spontaneous generosity.

The landlord of the pub set alight by the oil shop was not feeling like breakfast. He was worried and sought out Ken. 'Please,' he begged, 'Can you find my cash box, its contains all my money. It's in there,' pointing desperately to the still very hot ashes and rubble.

'That's a tall order. Whereabouts?' The landlord showed the area where it had been. Firemen cooled off the debris and, after diligent searching, unearthed the cash box. Before Ken could shout stop, he opened it eagerly to find his notes burnt to a cinder. Plunging his hand in, they floated into the air as charred paper. 'If only you had left them alone,' said Ken, 'the numbers could have been deciphered by an expert and you would have got your money back.' Afterwards, Ken confided, 'That man must have lost a small fortune as well as his pub.'

*   *   *

Before darkness fell on the Sunday night more bombs began to fall on the city, just as the sirens sounded. Ken and his townies were having their tea in a Rest Centre as the wail started. As they rushed back, twice they had to dive full length in the roadway to escape blast and debris.

Fortunately this raid did not last long – only a few hours! But, it was planned to hamper Civil Defence workers. Something like 200 delayed-action bombs were dropped.

'Watch out carefully, keep your eyes skinned,' warned Ken. 'Not all the DAs will be traced. You could well be working on a job and, unless you read the signs where they buried themselves, you won't know until they go bang.' The warnings spread fast, but still there were bound to be casualties. Fortunately, not too many that night.

Bomb disposal men came to Ken and asked, 'Can you pump out the water in that large crater? There's a DA at the bottom.' 'My God, you blokes have got guts,' replied Ken. So had the fire crew as they gingerly dropped their suction hose into the vast hole and started pumping.

Two more nights the Heinkels again made raids, although none was as heavy as the Saturday. Wednesday afternoon, Ken and his men paraded outside the battered station and were taken by fire tenders to Portsmouth, where they were given the luxury of a hot soak at the public baths. It was with the compliments of Southampton Corporation. No expensive gift could have been better.

'Thank you Southampton, you did everything you could for us,' said Ken to himself as he bathed himself clean.

The next morning Ken received instructions to take his men home. But, 'First, you must help in the clear up,' said the controlling officer. All available men were spread out, each group to cover a number of streets, to collect all gear and equipment now surplus to the work still going on, and roll up for collection all the lengths of discarded hose.

That was no easy task. In some streets there were as many as eight and nine lengths of hose, most had glass splinters embedded in them. There was much cursing and some casualties as they tried to roll them up.

Worst was to come for the men still there, as the Reading team hopped on their bus. At the fire stations all the hose had to be tested for holes, scrubbed clean of grit and glass and then dried. By evening time there was a washing line of hose, with particles of glass still embedded and scintillating like diamonds in the late sun.

*   *   *

'Blitz rolls!' Southampton gave its name to the early efforts to feed all the firemen who arrived as small groups from different counties. There was much cribbing at early blitzes from men who found no organisation to keep them fed, when they arrived at the end of long journeys. 'Don't forget it was a bloody sight worse when they came to Reading,' reminded Ken.

Nevertheless, they were hungry men and 'luncheon meat stuff', as they called it, and bread – that's all there was – quickly gained a place in history as 'Blitz rolls'.

But, while Ken's men, and many others were being instructed to make their way to a town school for the rolls, the London Fire Brigade brought their own canteen and food, with their fire-fighters. They were now well organised after being bloodied so badly at the start.

Ken's men spotted the canteen and swiftly joined the queue. 'Sorry, not for you, only London AFS,' said the girl, frantically trying to handle the crush. The Reading boys disappeared behind the canteen where some of the London men were taking a rest. 'Can we borrow your steel helmets?' They nodded, and, with a new identity, back into the queue, returning with soup, roll, and a welcome cup of tea.

*   *   *

Firemen moved to Testwood from a make-do reinforcing base, near Fareham, set up early in the blitz period. Testwood was a name known by now to all firemen as a

103

'home' where they waited to go into action, and later, in the NFS, as a training school.

Several hundred firemen would rally there at a time, usually staying two weeks. Letters, clean clothes, and pay, were taken down mid stay. Their vehicles parked easily in its large car park. The invasion threat was treated just as seriously, firemen stood guard at the gates, day and night – with pick-axe handles. 'What the hell we do if two or three Jerries come along with rifles, I don't know,' roused one man picked for the chore.

No Hudson Terraplane or comfortable little Morris for one group of Reading firemen on stand-by in the jittery invasion threat days. From Gowrings Garage action station, they travelled by builder's lorry. It saved their lives! Given a day's holiday, as a respite from action, they decided on an outing to Bournemouth.

It was another case of giving a learner driver a chance behind the wheel. 'Watch out, it's out of control,' shouted Bill, among those sitting in the open back. Within seconds it hit the bank and turned over twice, spinning round to face the opposite way. The builder's gantry behind the cab took the impact – and saved them from crushing.

Sitting beside the road recovering, Bill shouted, 'Blimey, it's the first time I have had a new pair of trousers and now look.' He and his friends were suffering from burn sores from the rubbing, and all had to go to hospital. But they were alive – enough for officers to want to know what they were doing with the lorry. It was the last day out in Bournemouth!

There were other characters among the contingents. One, Ben, was a tramp, he knew every workhouse in England, and his friend was just as much something special. With little to do when evenings stayed quiet, both lost all their money playing cards – and there was still a week to go.

Quietly they arranged a couple of hours off in the afternoon. They were looking for a way to make money. Wandering around the lanes, they saw apples on a tree. 'Can we buy some?' they asked the old fellow. 'No, help yourself.' They worked hard, returning with well over a hundredweight – and sold them to the chaps, making enough money to last the week!

Later in the NFS days, at a quiet time, the Reading men were give a day off. 'We can make it to Reading, if we can hitch a lift,' said one. All agreed. There was little traffic and it was hot walking along the main road. A lorry stopped, it was dirty and they had to sit in the back.

'I'm not going in that,' said Ben. They were well on their way to Reading when a hearse passed them. Sitting beside the coffin was Ben, he gave them a dignified wave. He was going to be home first.

*   *   *

Testwood became highly organised in the NFS days. Line up in the morning, with the commandant on the steps, 'It's just like the Army,' was the cry. Gordon was there with five crews, standing in front, while the orders were detailed. Canadian volunteer firemen were there as well. When the order came 'Dismiss' the Brits turned smartly to the right. Gordon could hear the Canadian officer say, 'All right chaps, break it up.'

Informal perhaps, but these Canadians were smart. The River Test ran through the grounds; its salmon were specially bred and fishing rights were expensive even in those days. At night they stood on its small bridge with ceiling hooks, borrowed from the fire vehicles. They were used to doing this at home, and swiftly three or four salmon were speared and cooked for supper.

Ken Watson had fun with the Canadians as well. He admired them for volunteering to come over to help fight the blitz, and appreciated Southampton giving them a civic welcome when they arrived, led by their own officers. It was just as the Luftwaffe eased up; soon they were feeling fed up, just like the AFS prior to the real war starting.

Hating parades, and rebellious, Ken talked them round to joining his fitness training. A length of six-inch steel pipe was used for log exercises. Amidst much chaffing and good humoured banter, Ken persuaded them, 'You eight go over and fetch the pipe.' The tallest took the ends, the rest in between, they groaned and moaned as though it was heavy and staggered to the start line.

The shortest wrapped his arms round the pipe and lifted his feet off the ground, two or three of the others let go and, ultimately, the two tallest were left, the others sauntering behind and kidding the carriers unmercifully. They were fit, and they were ready.

*   *   *

Shortly after the 'fire engine' taxi crashed, one of the first of the ATVs, as the Austin towing vehicles were to be called, 'posh' in its shiny grey paint, replaced it. The other stations were also welcoming the Austins like winning racehorses.

They were in time for many of the long journeys. For the drivers it was a welcome change. They could even steer! Heavy pumps dragging down the rear of softly sprung luxury cars almost took the front wheels off the ground. No longer were they passing dejected AFS crews, useless at the side of the road, because of broken springs and burnt out clutches, caused by the unequal task put on the cars. The driver's hardest task now was to cope with the varied gearboxes fitted, there could be no delay for standardisation.

But what was wrong with the crews? Every journey they were arriving sleepy and sick? Fumes from the exhausts were being drawn into the back of the vans! Heavy curtains were hurriedly fitted: jump in, pull them across and everything was fine. The men loved their ATVs as much as they did their Home Office pumps.

Ken Watson was having a drink with a pilot friend, home on leave. Both were light-heartedly putting the world to rights. Then, the pilot said, 'I don't know much about your bunch down there but you want your heads examined!' Always the professional, Ken listened. 'You have gloss paint on everyone of those new vans. When I am flying at night and there is the slightest moon, we can see you shining like a lot of little moonbeams. Jerry can see you easily.'

Ken realised how vulnerable they were to attack. Knock-out a column of fire fighters, it must be attractive to the Luftwaffe. Immediately he passed on the news. Frantically, workshops set about blacking the roofs. Keen to get his done, Ken asked for paint. His offer was gratefully received.

But, when he was hard at the task himself with a messenger, a senior officer arrived at his station. 'Station inspection,' he said. Back at HQ he reported, 'What do you think I found. Your station officer in an old pair of overalls with a paint brush, working with a messenger. What are you doing in this division?' 'How can we ever win?' Ken asked John later.

*   *   *

Further heavy raids on Plymouth, Clydeside, and then three on Liverpool, made Ken realise that Hitler was asking the Luftwaffe to make systematic attacks on the ports receiving the Atlantic convoys. 'Perhaps the ports on the Bristol Channel will get more attacks? That means more trips for us.' He wrote as he thought, adding Wokingham have just had a pump damaged in Bristol.

In fact it was five nights attacking Plymouth, he carefully recorded a note in his diary. More bombs fell on Reading on Saturday night, but, thankfully, the incidents continued to be small.

Then London was hit, this was a major raid – in fact the city's last great raid but that could only have been wishful thinking at that moment. Just like Portsmouth, the glow in the sky told anxious firemen's wives where their husbands had gone.

Ken had just written 'The threat of invasion seems to have receded,' when through the door came a Ministry of Information leaflet. Every house got one. Winston Churchill made time to write the 'personal' message with the 'What to do' instructions if the Germans invade. 'For all of you,' he wrote, 'then the order and the duty will be: "Stand firm".'

*   *   *

Ken's question, 'How long before fire brigades are united?' was being answered behind the scenes in London. The need for reform of fire brigades was no longer just a hot potato, it was one that had to be grasped. Everything else was burning, apart from the politicians' hands.

Countless stories of quotations from civic dignitaries in 1938 and 39, when the Home Office wanted greater changes under the new Act, were repeated endlessly. Like the council in London which refused a car for their fire officer to be able to move quickly around the docks. 'He was not going to have him spending his time riding round, it was not necessary,' declared an alderman. It was, when the officer was in the thick of it and wanted to move from one trouble spot to others.

They even came from as far away as Wincanton, in rural Somerset, where the councillors had been told that two men always on duty was the minimum. Several members felt the expense was not justified. They decided that the cheapest way was to have four full-time men on 12 hour shifts – 'on the understanding that they would get relief in the evenings from voluntary auxiliary part-time firemen'.

But now, that May-time vicious attack on London, with outside fire brigades called in, had everybody vocal.

Pressure from above was growing on civic authorities. Something had to be done to bring together the reinforcing crews when they were in action. Working as individual crews, they knew themselves, that team work would bring better results. Especially difficult was knowing who was really experienced when giving orders – especially with so many 'Admirals' in the fancy uniforms of the volunteer fire brigades, who were working as willingly, and living as dangerously, as the AFS.

At last, too, the pressure was on to bring in women. Many brigades had resisted the intrusion into a man's world. But, the word was let the women operate the control rooms, get the experienced officers out into the action.

There were other amazing stories of cities, like London, where women were always part of the action – and dying like men. Top of the list were firewomen driving petrol tankers through fire-swept streets, for hours on end, topping up the pumps. And another driving a double-decker bus regularly as a canteen van, regardless of the danger.

In London, in the first September blitz, an AFS girl won the George Medal. She volunteered to take petrol in a van through intense bombing so that pumps could be refuelled.

In Reading it was the men who had been feeling the pressure since Margaret and her friends, had moved into the control room after Dunkirk. Let them be seen dallying to talk to the girls and they were in trouble! But 1941 was to see momentous change.

15 · 'Total war' – NFS

Another sleepless night. There was no need for telephones to tell the people in The Thames Valley that London was taking another pounding. The sirens had everybody on the alert as the raiders seemed to drone endlessly overhead and all who wanted, and some who didn't, could watch the gunflashes and searchlights and, in the distance, that frightening glow.

But still there was no call for Caversham to give assistance, the famous London Fire Brigade had got itself as well organised as possible. 'We are still not wanted,' said John Lander. He sounded disappointed: it was human when alerted by the purple and red warnings, and yet standing around, helpless.

'At least they know now how to control their aid. All our little groups rushing in all over the place must have added to the chaos, even though we were desperately needed,' grunted Ken Watson.

'Remember when that first call for help was made? Some are still talking about the fire brigade from the Midlands which didn't arrive until the next day,' recalled John. 'They spent the time polishing the engine's brass because they were proud to be going to London!'

'I can't vouch for it but the lobby to bring all the fire brigades together – there are more than 1,600 of them – seems to be winning,' said Ken. 'There are plenty of hints in Parliament and suggestions in the newspapers – and The Times seems to be having a go.' He was ready to talk; all preparations for the night were made, and the waiting seemed the worst. 'It makes sense to me, mind you I am not a regular fireman, and a lot of the chiefs and the brass hats must wonder what will happen to them if it does.

'Churchill says we're fighting a total war, so why don't we?'

John laughed again. 'Do you also remember when that volunteer brigade fire chief came to Reading? Gold braid, silver epaulettes, white lanyard and whistle, and four gold bands on his sleeves and gold oak leaves on his cap. Truly, a magnificent figure.'

'Yes, but don't forget that they are important figures in their own communities,' responded Ken. 'I bet men like that wouldn't wish to be small fish in a big fire brigade.

'Don't forget too, most like that have efficient stations, and almost all are paid for by local subscriptions.'

The next night Ken and John were ready again. Suddenly they realised that London was escaping, the first time for 76 nights. 'Notch that up,' said Ken.

But it was not the end. May 10, London suffered its 500th – 'and one of the worst raids,' was Tom Goldsmid's report. The rumblings from that great fire of London seemed to bring things to a head. Three days later the Home Secretary announced a new NFS, National Fire Service, and sweeping reforms.

The local authorities bowed to the inevitable; they were told it was not to be a permanent reorganisation. On the 13th the Home Secretary announced the decision to the House of Commons. Ken reading the newspaper report saw him pay 'a very sincere tribute of admiration for their conspicuous personal courage and skill' to regulars and AFS.

The next paragraph caught his eye, he re-read it, and paraphrased it in his mind. The Government was convinced that drastic change must be made to meet air attacks of the scale experienced. 'That means we are going to get a lot more!' he said to himself.

*   *   *

The way the Battle on the Home Front was going was worrying politicians who made up the united Government. Censorship of news, so that Hitler and his Nazis should not know how devastating was their bombing, was having a disastrous affect at home. People suffering the most were dispirited when the wireless and newspapers were dismissive of their suffering and the extent of the damage. The reality was that it was all part of the total war effort to make the German bombers think they were failing. Some firemen, too, were feeling that strain – after all they were ordinary men and women.

*   *   *

Plans went ahead at great speed. In August 1941 all the brigades in England and Wales were nationalised. Vital efforts were being made to back up the brave men with the right equipment. No longer were there two masters, councils and the Home Office.

'It's been like an army fighting with guns and bullets that don't match, and bayonets which can't even be clipped on to the rifles!,' said Ken as they quietly cheered the good news. 'I reckon there are plenty of civic leaders throughout the country, and some local fire chiefs, who are not too pleased this morning.'

But the men were who had been answering the blitz calls. Proud of their AFS status – and their epic efforts – they knew that nationalisation was necessary. Across the country nothing was standardised, equipment on the motley fire engines, supplies, working hours, mobilising, and, especially, hydrant fittings – an exasperating problem creating most despair when fighting a fire in a strange town. How it would all be sorted out was going to be a battle in itself.

It was a tribute that the new red and black NFS tunic badges, and the silver buttons, were exactly the same design as the original AFS. And there was less trouble sewing them on than scrabbling to sew up a strange water supply!

Messenger Harold Randle received his without really understanding the excitement and the conversation it was creating. He had been in long enough to recognise

109

the make-do-and-mend necessity of the war-time firemen, but, being at a complete AFS action station, he was used to handling equipment most of which was standardised among such stations. Except for the dammed collection of hydrant standpipes and keys which had to be carried.

There were standpipes with a ball fitting to release the water, others with bayonet lugs to clamp on to the main, some with V screws, others with round threads, and, frustration on frustration, hydrant pits too deep for the AFS equipment to reach the water main! And valve keys with many varying sizes of spindles – so it was often impossible to turn the water on, even if the standpipe fitted!

As far as Harold could see, there was one bigger problem even than that. Many hydrants were not marked! If you weren't a local, everyone wasted time scouting round trying to find the tiny metal covers. He was going to learn that as a hard lesson!

*   *   *

The plane crash on top of the famous Streatley Hills was a night he would never forget. U-station, as Tilehurst was now to be called, was awakened by the telephone call. 'Send major pump AND mobile dam and light pump . . . ' Both were on the board available BUT there was only one crew, expecting to be asked to take one or the other!

Plane crashes meant all speed possible, and it was a long way away in that language. There were two drivers, Jack said he could take the mobile dam, but crew?

Harold butted into the tense deliberation with an answer. 'I can ride with Jack, I know what to do.' One quick look from Roger Smith, now a section leader. 'Good idea. Jack get your gear off the major pump.' He turned to the leading fireman, 'Get away with the pump, fast. Jack follow on with the dam. Fill up with water when you get to Streatley.'

Travelling with a canvas dam filled with 500 gallons of water, supported in its metal frame and riding loose on the lorry's floor, was lethal if a driver picked up speed. The practice was to get near the trouble fast and then fill up.

Streatley came up fast. But where is there a hydrant? Both Jack and Harold were straining out of the windows seeking, but not finding. They stopped, straddling the crossroads. On their feet they still had no luck. Time was running out. 'If only hydrants were marked,' said Harold.

'We shall have to cross the river to Goring,' muttered Jack. 'Quick, see if we can get the pump off and push it back up the slope, so I can turn the lorry.' Snapping out the handles, both took the strain as Jack pulled out the towing pin. Harold realised the lorry was moving. 'Jack, the lorry's running away!'

Frantically, Jack scampered to catch up with it; he dived head first through the still open cab door and grabbed the brake. It stopped on the pavement, just feet from the fence and a big drop into the field beyond.

Harold watched, he could not move, he was balancing the pump on his own, and Jack rushed back. He was white, a lot of explaining had been saved by quick reactions, and a few inches. 'Thanks kid. I couldn't have put the brake on properly. It was the pump brake which was holding the lorry.'

Across the river, there was another frantic search until finally a hydrant was found and the dam filled. Then they set off crawling up Streatley Hill, it was as if all in slow motion. When they arrived, the fire was out. A Spitfire night fighter was the casualty, broken and on its back. But the fire had never really got hold and the hard-found 500 gallons was not wanted.

In the morning, at the office, Harold told the Editor of the plane crash. 'Find out the details, write a report. We will take a picture and then see if we can publish. That means another trip for you to the censor's office.'

*　　*　　*

The critics often had a field day as such massive plans for an NFS were put into operation. It was a monumental task. Probably the quickest administration revolution in modern history. Officers changed jobs, with many high-placed ranks coming out of London to the very different world of Britain's countryside. Fire brigades united in a way impossible to think of before that Government edict. Although to be fair, neighbours generally had become very good at helping each other.

The idea was to bring them all under Home Office control; England and Wales being split into 43 Fire Forces. Berkshire joining Bucks and Oxon and becoming No 15. The Secretary of State delegated Donald M Taylor, from the famous Fleet Street station in London, to be the Fire Force Commander. He set too with gusto, with his initial headquarters at the Maidenhead fire station, later at White Place, Taplow.

In turn three fire forces were controlled by a Chief Regional Officer, and H M Smith, the Home Office inspector, who had worked so hard, was appointed. This was covering the established Civil Defence set-up, where the Government's Regional Commissioner included the fire service among his references.

Truly a nationalisation which was considered, but impossible, two years earlier.

All the fire services in 15 Fire Force, big and small, suddenly found themselves parts of four divisions, the same was going on all over the country. These in turn were sorted into sub divisions. Every station had a number and these were stencilled on to all appliances and fire pumps. Immediately people knew where any unit came from – and where it was.

Reading, for example, became the centre for A Division with Reading's chief officer as divisional officer, controlling a much wider area, including several volunteer brigades. The huge red engines at the main station – which had never been allowed out of town to go to the blitzes – suddenly became very equal with the war-time units: 15 A 1 Z was their white-painted sign. The 1 signified the first sub-division. But they stayed red, and kept the Reading Fire Brigade insignia.

At Ken's Caversham station everything was marked the same but with a final V, 'For Victory,' was Ken's belief. The letters worked back from the end of the alphabet. Harold's being U-station. The old fire station in The Butts was named Y;

111

the garage in Wokingham Road, W; Gowrings garage on the main London Road – the route through the town for thousands of pre-war holidaymakers – stencilled X.

A 1 T was Henley; R, Wallingford; and Q, Didcot. Sonning and Pangbourne, the part-timers, were S and P. Soon there was to be a night-only station, at Bakers Garage, off Friar Street, in the heart of the town centre, manned entirely by part-timers. Appropriately it became O – for overtime, some thought.

Others to change included the old Wokingham volunteers; Wargrave, once run by the parish council; Newbury, Hungerford, Wantage and Lambourn.

No longer were councils involved; the NFS was responsible for its own administration. Men to handle the immensity of this as well as operational officers were appointed. A finance officer sorted out the spending – and the pay; an establishments officer put together records of every man, to find talent, and those who would benefit from more training. Stores and transport were other vital posts. And, of course, catering – at last real efforts were to be made to see that men fed properly.

Despite Ken's enthusiasm for the change, and although appointed as Company Officer, he was soon to start cribbing at the way it worked. 'I have counted more than 78 forms to be filled in at our station level!' he groaned at John, now a Section Leader.

But the important business was that fire engines could be moved without delay where needed. At the Fire Force headquarters, as at other control centres, women came into their own. Every pump which was manned and operational was known, whether it was at a fire, on exercise, or standing ready and waiting for Hitler.

Their own Battle of Britain planning was complete. Now let the German bombers come, the NFS is ready to fight back.

It was. Those at Fire Force control answered the pleas for help, or, indeed, would be ready to call for assistance. No need now to ask civic authorities, 'Can or Will you send aid?' Those cities and towns being bombed, and needing reinforcements from outside their own region, simply asked the Home Office Fire Control room in London and it was on its way.

By now the war-time special pump-escapes, and huge self-propelled Sulzer, Coventry and Tangye pumps which could produce 1,000 gallons a minute, were at various stations. The 'guns' which could handle the 'ammunition' were making it possible to stem many of the fires which got away in the early blitzes.

16 · NFS Jigsaw

Blitzkrieg on Russia! Hitler surprised the world, yet again, with that June fury. While the frenetic efforts at home were putting together the first easy pieces of the NFS jigsaw, and there were not many like that, the Luftwaffe moved airfields and the bombing offensive eased. Whatever the Nazi leader's thinking, his attack to the East gave the British Isles a life-line. A respite, and time to put things together again. Especially for the firemen.

They had just withstood the heaviest attack on London, when the sky seemed full of bombers and the ground to be erupting continuously; followed by continuous nights of blitzes on Plymouth and Devonport – incredible fires seen beyond the high-rising famous moors – then major attacks on Portsmouth.

The most violent of the Luftwaffe's raids turned to cause further devastation on Plymouth, before switching North. London's further major attack, just before the NFS announcement, was followed by heavy bombing of Birmingham.

From that night, bombers kept coming, but not in armadas: they were back to raids on factories, especially those building aircraft.

Hitler's decision, and the lessening of bombing raids, could not be believed at first. There was no time to be lost in building an organisation. 'Do you realise that the new Fire Force Commander has probably had no more than three weeks to collect his thoughts and plan,' was Ken Watson's reaction as he discussed the monumental change with John Lander.

Practical John could see one big improvement. 'At least we change to 24 hours on and 24 hours off, that will be far more civilised,' he replied.

*   *   *

Transformation of so many brigades, council and voluntary, into a national service would mean speedy co-ordination, and making use of all resources. To get that set up people all across the country were hurriedly finding buildings to be controlling headquarters.

Where could be housed the divisional headquarters, centred on Reading? That kind of question was being asked in every county. Home Office planners had pin-pointed Maidenhead for Fire Force HQ. It was part of Region No 6 and that would stay in Reading at Marlborough House.

Prospect Park Mansion, was standing empty. High on the top land of one of the town's large parks, it was visually exciting as a Georgian house from the outside. But, inside! It had been standing disused, far removed from its former glory.

Gas lamps had given it elegance in its time but they tried eyes and tempers as teams cleared the house and quickly brought A Division HQ into operation.

It was also the moment when women took on a major role. Not only bringing their finesse to many mobilising tasks, control room, and now necessary clerical and catering, but also taking on men's work.

They were a breath of fresh air. Not all the men would agree with that but they brought laughter into a service which had been able to do nothing but take itself seriously and battle to survive.

As it took shape, Henry Barnes, the former 'brass hat', whose memory was long, told irritated opponents, 'This legislation is the finest thing that has happened to the fire service.' His ability and knowledge of the area was recognised at Divisional HQ.

That was not quite the view of the cook when she arrived. 'There's one slop bucket to cope with the cooking as well as the washing up!'

*   *   *

Every pump available was logged with the control of the NFS. A look at the mobilising boards at Region, Fire Force, or each of the divisional HQs, told the story of the day. No longer a casual note in the day book that some men had gone to Portsmouth, Southampton, Birmingham, wherever they were risking their lives.

Exercises were staged to make sure that convoys of pumps were ready to move off when and wherever needed. To make the system work, some were on paper, particularly to test the firewomen, but most by turning out the crews.

Years of individuality were being pressed into one mould. The phone rang in the station at one of Berkshire's villages. A girl's voice told the former fire chief, 'Mobilise your appliance and report to the fire station at Rugby for Coventry.' Time ... and the rest of the jargon followed. No pleasantries, just one of the newly formalised messages.

Later realising that she had heard no more; no report of the men being on the way, the girl rang again. The same officer answered. 'Has your pump gone?' 'Oh, I thought you were playing!' was his shocked reply. He believed it was yet another communications exercise.

*   *   *

Ordered back to get some sleep at a rest station, Ken, as company officer, and his crews were grateful. They had been at work for 48 hours, not as long as some of the men already there when they arrived. But, the men from Reading had been up for 24 hours before they started on the road.

Men were lying in heaps all over the floor when they got there. 'They're dead, right out on their feet,' he said to the fireman beside him. He was new to the blitz. His eyes opened wider, he really had thought the men were dead! At that moment there was a whistling sshsh, and the fireman was on his face under a table. 'What's up with you?' asked Ken curtly. 'I thought it was a bomb.' 'It was a train whistle!'

114

Ken turned to Tom Goldsmid from his own crew. 'I can't stand this and I can't keep my eyes open. Let's go into our vehicle.' Ken pulled himself into the driver's seat. He was out.

Minutes later Tom was shaking him furiously. 'Guv'nor, For Christ's sake get out of the car. A DAs gone in across the road, it will go off any time.' He kept shaking, trying to wake Ken. 'Leave me alone, I have got to get some sleep.'

'We all do. Get out,' grunted a very worried Tom, and he pulled his officer out of the seat and half-dragged him back into the building, and sat him on a sack. For five hours Ken did not move, he slept without knowledge of the delayed-action bomb. With a groan, he tried to open his eyes; every bone in his body ached. He felt the sack, it was full of potatoes. Seconds later he was asleep again as Tom tried to protect him as the others crept up to see this tough man beaten at last.

When fire crept up on the building, reaction got Ken moving again. But many other men were sleeping oblivious, lying in water, as others fought the flames and tried to rouse them. There was still plenty of fire-fighting to be done, even if many bombers were in the snow of Russia.

*   *   *

Although relieved that men and machines were knitted into a powerful weapon to fight the blitzes, big problems still faced D M Taylor, and the other Fire Force Commanders like him. Workshops, building department, uniform store and repairs, hose repair, and accommodation, were all big headaches if the NFS was to operate effectively. Communications! Water! were top of the list.

The early blitzes saw cast-iron water mains in the ground fracture as high-explosive bombs 'moved' the ground. Lengths of steel piping laid along the streets were used with success to renew supplies to the firefighters. Even if hit and broken, another length could be clamped into place and water flowed again. Enormous lorries were pressed into service to carry pipes where most needed.

By the time Donald Taylor took up his command, he was able to press ahead with plans to provide ready laid pipelines to all his major towns.

Already the colossal emergency water supply tanks were being put into place. EWS, in huge white letters within a St Andrew's cross, ensured everyone would know where to find water. One stood at The Triangle, next to the Co-op departmental stores, the Odeon Cinema and Palace Theatre, another in the grounds of Battle Hospital, two vital spots.

Some, at X-station, were trained to handle the immense task of providing these water supplies. It was a sight everyone came to accept, and small boys to enjoy! Pipelines ran from both the Thames and the Kennet in the town centre.

From the Thames the six-inch pipe worked its way along Caversham Road, through West Street into the town centre. All the road junctions were dug up and angled pipes welded so that it disappeared beneath the surface and rose again the other side. The other from the Kennet covered the Duke Street end of town. Another fed south, all the way up London Street to Whitley. All over the south of England this major feat of simple, if unsightly, engineering was taking place.

At intervals firemen had to break the joints so that rubbish which collected in the gutters could be cleared. Small boys were always ready for this, sometimes it might be a shilling, a fortune, and not a penny, which could be 'rescued' if they pounced quickly.

*   *   *

Ken Watson was livid, he was hitting the roof with righteous anger. John was not saying a word, he was in full agreement. Ken was just back from Southampton, where he had taken a convoy of pumps for more action.

To keep together, convoys were told to travel at a set speed. Knowing the road, and the hills, from frequent visits, Ken instructed his driver to travel faster down the hills so as to climb the other side without wasting time. It was a skill, with the weight of the pumps dragging behind.

A former none-too-popular 'brass hat' was waiting and watching in a side turning as they passed. He reported Ken's driver for exceeding the speed limit – not Ken for giving the order.

There was already an angry difference between Ken and the new service. An officer had taken one of Ken's drivers out at the controls of a big red machine. 'Would you like a cigarette? 'Thank you, sir.' As soon as it was lit, 'You are on a charge, you know you are not supposed to smoke on these machines.'

'Didn't I let fly,' said Ken when he came back from headquarters. 'Charges be damned, they were scrapped.' He shook his head. 'What's happening to the NFS? You've got to be Yes men, to get on.' His ardour to keep sense in a service was not popular to many, but it was to those who mattered and he was promoted. His new role was to encompass many of the new problems facing the NFS as the country-side of the three counties was transformed into vital bases and airfields. Britain was hitting back, and the United States had come to our aid.

*   *   *

Like Ken, Gordon Castle still retained the pleasure of remembering the way his men transformed Hamilton Road Garage to set-up the Wokingham Road action station. When they moved in they were sitting on an empty petrol storage tank, with grease-caked repair workshop and mess room. Loads of caustic soda brought the boards up white. A harder task was getting a dormitory constructed. But, there was a big bonus – a hoist and all the garage equipment.

Now in the NFS, as better, more powerful, vehicles were provided, Gordon's men were able to hoist them on the ramp to clean and service, and spray them grey. Later, as the action died away, and the NFS became organised, Gordon made use of the talents of a fireman who was a sign-writer by trade.

The cars were really smart, with professional red lines on the grey and other writing and station numbers. But, each time, it was taken for headquarters's transport. Gordon was mad, and said so. His station was given a brand new Buick Straight Eight, cigar lighter and all in the fittings, as a towing car – and one that

116

Gordon, as the station's officer, could use himself. It seemed almost a shame to have to spray its black paintwork grey.

Clearly decisions were made to meet conditions! 'Or is it the other way round,' thought Gordon.

*   *   *

A massive building programme was started with great speed. The need to provide reinforced concrete control rooms was one major task. These were added in all the stations. Better protection meant the NFS could keep control of its fire-fighting.

Gordon's W-station was chosen as secondary sub-divisional control, in case Z-station was bombed. The control room was built to cope with that. The house next door was taken over and used as quarters for the girls manning the control.

Most of the stations taken over from volunteer brigades, as well as the action stations such as in Reading, were totally unsuitable for whole-time manning. Priority was given to providing additional accommodation, usually pre-fabricated huts, on site, or within 'running distance'.

At U-station Harold Randle saw the control room extended and strengthened very quickly. Another night, when he came on duty, it was to find three new sets of double-doors bashed through that sombre long front wall. Now any first-call machine could go out without time-wasting.

Across the main road, behind the Co-op store, on a piece of waste ground, foundations were going in for a prefabricated wooden Army-type hut. It looked large. 'Dormitory, rest room and kitchens,' Roger Smith told him. 'We are going to have a woman cook, as well.'

It certainly was running distance, but at last the men were being looked after. Overcoats as well! But, something is missing, thought Harold. Simple really, although the sirens still disturbed the night, the raiders were harassing, not menacing. Most times in the South it seemed they came as a handful not a hundred or more. The heavy raids were to the North. Still the NFS in the region was readying itself, everybody expected the Luftwaffe to be back – and soon.

No doubt Hitler wanted to as well. The heavy bombing of his own cities was angering him but the demands of the Russian front, and the Mediterranean, meant he had to take his own medicine.

17 · Women – tough time

With the formation of the National Fire Service the few women who volunteered at the time of Dunkirk found themselves no longer so heavily outnumbered. Britain was completely on a war footing. Fads about what women could and could not do were thrown away – forever.

Jane was the daughter of the owner of a large transport company, which was busy carrying workers, day and night, to munitions and aircraft factories. She could drive, still a rare feat in 1941. Up to the war was a time when the middle class could afford a small car, but the working man achieved a motor cycle, or, more likely, a cycle or used the buses.

There was no hesitation from the transport officer at divisional headquarters to this firewoman of a fortnight. 'I want you to come to Y-Station,' he said. When they arrived in The Butts, he was equally brief. 'Take that fire engine to Caversham Road station. 'It was the heavy pre-war RD 111, the workhorse of the mid-thirties. Still painted red, but with mudguards and bumpers outlined in white to help show in the dark, it was a giant.

Jane's face was almost as bright red. Shock? Surprise? Anger? He thought because her father had a big fleet that she could drive such heavy vehicles! Her own achievement was much more modest, a motor car.

But, she was made of stern stuff and was not going to be shown up by such a brusque man. She climbed up the running board to the driver's place, perched herself on the very edge of the leather cushion of the bench seat, and stretched out to reach the massive steering wheel.

With that he was gone, and Jane was very much alone. She looked down to the middle of the floor, there was no gear lever and she realised that the long lever on the offside was it! And it was a gate change! No wonder he had shouted, 'Don't forget to double declutch,' as he drove off!

Straight through the town centre streets she drove. People gaped, they had never before seen a huge fire engine with a woman driver, all alone. Jane got there, safely. 'How do we do these things?' she asked her friend Betty, back at headquarters.

Betty, although like Jane officially in communications, had volunteered to learn at the NFS driving school at Bray. She confided that only the previous week she had been frightened out of her own life.

'I had only just got back from the course when the same officer walked into the telephone control room and said, 'You are going to take a lorry to Elstree.' That was 40-plus miles away. 'Me?' asked Betty. 'Yes, you've passed out all right.' 'Well I'm going to pass out now,' was her reply, she told Jane.

'I was really scared when I got into that lorry. Fixed seat and my short legs. I sat like this and I really had no control,' and she dangled her legs from her perch on the canteen table. 'The lorry was loaded with motor bikes, and they were hanging over each side.

'I don't know how I got there. When I reached the narrow iron bridge crossing the canal in Slough there was an Army convoy coming the other way. But they stopped and let me through.

'I was in a trance by the time I reached Elstree, and I don't remember much about them unloading the bikes. I do remember on the way back I ran over a dog in Maidenhead, that was sad. I wasn't sure of the law, but people said I could not have done anything about it.'

Jane paused before replying. 'Well, they are not going to beat us.' She meant it. It was a good thing she did because it was not long before she was again called from control. This time to take a lorry laden with desks and chairs to London.

Like most people, Jane had never driven through London. 'I don't know where I am going,' she thought quietly to herself as the brief instructions were given, 'It's off Oxford Street, near the Palladium.'

'Imagine me sailing down Oxford Street, trying to spot the street,' she told Betty afterwards. 'I turned right, it was the right street but it was a one-way street! Everybody was shouting at me and I had to back out into Oxford Street and find a way round.'

In no time she was regularly driving a hose-laying lorry, keeping a steady pace as the endless lengths of hose fed out behind her.

Betty was to face another strange journey across the Berkshire Downs at night during the next winter. Sent to give the Didcot firemen a lecture on how to handle messages on their fire calls, she knew she would be anything but popular when she arrived. Betty was not looking forward to it.

For miles she followed the one red light at the rear of the longest RAF convoy she had ever met. There was no way of passing. Suddenly her worries ceased, her car broke down. The fact that she was marooned in the cold and dark seemed less of a problem in the strange world of 1942.

*   *   *

The toughness of the tasks facing the firewomen were taken for granted: everybody was involved. It was as Churchill had said, 'Total war'. But with their arrival, in smart blue uniforms with shiny buttons, collars and ties, and black stockings, smiles of appreciation crept back into the tired faces of the blitz fighters.

Laughter – and love – were bonuses, some wanted, others unwanted. Ken shook his head in disgust. He did not like women on his station, and it was mutual. But, more important, he did not like the goings-on of a few, especially people drafted in with the NFS changes – 'Just like an Army abroad,' he muttered to John.

Ken blew his top when, visiting another station, he took a short cut back to his car. A fireman barred his way, 'Sorry, you can't go through there, sir.' He could, and he did. Inside he found an officer and a woman on the ground. Sniffing his disgust, he walked through. 'Spoilt their day,' he told John.

Harold, involved in a big three counties week-end exercise, stood puzzled in the drill yard as firemen scampered up a ladder and across the flat roof of the office. Somehow it seemed surreptitious. Back they came, and huddled in muffled conversation. Another man was called, more whispering, something about an officer and a firewoman, and up the ladder he ran and across the roof. He peered down through a perspex skylight, snorted and came back. He was angry, 'I forgot my bloody glasses!'

*   *   *

Bedroom space was scarce at Prospect Park Mansion as the shifts kept round-the-clock cover. Two sisters had their bunks in a bathroom. Putting her leg out of bed Enid could reach the tap and turn on a bath – it was a luxury few others had. Down below would echo, a fireman's voice, 'Lady Godiva's having her bath.'

Quite a big mansion, 'Loonies one side, intelligent people the other,' was often the cry. Loony might be the cry but the real problem, as the organisation settled down, was the missing, racing, adrenalin of the pre-NFS days. Hitler was not playing – yet. He was expected every day.

'Join the Gestapo,' was the whispered cry at the Park. The badge of membership was the A-division rubber date stamp – stamped as far up the firewoman's leg as the man could get, or the girl would let him! French knickers fashioned from parachute silk often replaced the serious service issue, and made the 'battle for the bottom' more exciting. It was just fun. Who knew when the Luftwaffe would strike again.

Regulations against fraternising were strict, especially accommodation areas. So too, going out after lights out – or coming in. The mansion's entrance porch, beneath which in happier days coaches used to halt, for visitors to step out in the dry, found a new use. A ladder, casually left, enabled determined souls to reach its roof and then enter through a window.

Laughingly Enid was making it scary for a new girl. 'Don't worry, you can keep your honour, it's just bomb-happy fun. 'Make sure you aren't caught out like I was.'

Enid went on to tell how on a crazy day, she was picked up and sat in the kitchen sink! 'I was furious. I got a bowl of dirty water and threw it as they came back round the corner. Only it wasn't the culprits – it was the divisional officer!'

She talked herself out of that one. Enid had an impeccable background. Her mother had been cook for the late King Edward when he was Prince of Wales. Enid had been a nanny with the Royal family at Windsor and she used to enthrall them with her stories of Eton's boys' day and the fireworks.

Her sister, Esther, was a lady's housekeeper and they had left London and come to Reading and volunteered. 'The day this war ends my sister and I are going back to London, come what may,' she told the new girl. It was a determination to come true.

Gordon Castle was enjoying a walk in his own garden. He was in his bedroom slippers – it was such a relief for a few hours from his rubber boots. Somehow feet seemed to swell to fit wellingtons, and socks to shrivel.

But trouble would not stay away. Two Spitfires flashing over collided, and Gordon could see where one was crashing. Still in his slippers, he ran across the fields from Whitley to Grazeley to see if he could help. There it was blazing in a house garden, the pilot looked dead.

Firemen arrived from Wokingham as he did. Their standpipe would not fit the hydrant. It did not matter, there was nothing they could do. Gordon shook his head, the early war scenario still existed. 'Just think, that could just as easily have been in my garden, or my house,' he said to the leading fireman.

*   *   *

Not everybody was happy with the formation of the NFS. Many of the fire chiefs of their own town brigades, suddenly found themselves 'relegated' to leading firemen or section leaders. Rank was related to the number of machines a man would control.

'Chips with everything,' was Henry Barnes comment as he endeavoured to liaise and bring everyone together. 'They all train differently, and I have got to take and distribute these typed sheets of instructions. I need danger money!'

*   *   *

Harrowing though the sight of dead WAAF girls was to the firemen fighting the British bomber crash on the aerodrome, it could numb the senses for only a short time. There was forever plenty of action, the same measure of 'excitement', and numerous frightening sights. There was also a need for sheer guts and strength on top of the all-too-quickly learned skills.

What fireman, when he volunteered as a civvy AFS, to defend his country had pictured himself faced with our own bombs blasting off around him? Yet, as the war was carried back to Germany, it was happening all too often.

Sirens still sounded but now the action seemed to come at any time. Most planes seemed to crash in remote spots! No convenience of roads to the aerodrome, and a handy, if insufficient water supply.

Gordon said, 'We were lucky to escape.' He was talking to his new deputy Pat Bird. Both had their hands wrapped round a mug of hot, strong tea.

They were back from a Lancaster crashed in the middle of a ploughed field. In trouble, it aborted a raid over Northern France and came back with a full bomb load. The plane was an inferno as the firemen scrambled through the mud. Some dragged hose, others humped cans of foam on their shoulders.

There was no sign of the bomber's crew – 'Thank God they've escaped,' said Gordon. They had only been there minutes when a RAF lorry came bouncing madly over the field. 'Get out,' shouted the driver, there are bombs on board!'

Gordon called his men away. 'We got 60 yards when the whole damn lot went up with a hell of an explosion.'

He sipped, as he thought, 'We were too near to get the full blast. That garage copped it 400 yards away, and the houses in the village.

'Just think, too, those bombs had been laying in that inferno for 15 minutes. Another time they go off on impact.' 'Sometimes they don't go off at all,' mused Pat. 'Therefore, we have to take the risk,' said Gordon.

It was only hours later that the station's bells were ringing again. It seemed a copycat situation, only this time the Lancaster managed to land at a nearby aerodrome. One or two bombs went off, the others thrown out in the crash were laying all around the wreckage.

'Big fat, juicy 500 pounders,' was Gordon's description. They were left alone! Next morning it would be the turn of the bomb disposal men to show their bravery. 'Yet those that did go off left a large crater, and blew a nearby farm building to smithereens.' He was puzzled.

18 · Sticky problem

Rationing was the tightest yet; everywhere prospects looked grim, but, to the experts, the NFS really was looking ready. 'Winter is on us again,' was the mundane miserable thought of many a fireman, it brought back harsh memories. Making their own fun was top action in their minds, free of the responsibility of the high decisions still being made. Then December seemed to bring strange 'sunshine'.

Russia surprised Hitler with a counter offensive; the Japanese devastated Pearl Harbour and attacked our bases in the Far East; the Americans declared war in reply, so did the Germans and Italians on America. Suddenly Britain was no longer alone.

Ken Watson's diary was filling its pages as 1941 ended. In October he had written with feeling, 'Yellow and white warnings have been scrapped.' In November, 'Larger night scale activity has started again.'

For the stations, it was time to think of parties for Christmas – 'How times have changed?' said Roger Smith to young Harold. The messenger was secretary of his station's entertainments committee. Everybody was determined to have a good time at all the stations, it looked as though there might be a good chance. Jane trained a troupe of young girls and they were in great demand. There was fun at the Mansion House. But, all the time the guard was kept up. Firemen and women were on duty, in case the Luftwaffe attacked.

At the back of Jane's mind, and others, was brewing an idea, a big concert to show people in the town there was talent in the Civil Defence. And to raise money for charity as well as keep up morale. But that was to come later.

*   *   *

The handbell ringers were entertaining at the Slough station, it was a grand party. The firemen were joining in the spirit with determination. Some were dressed as women, wigs, skirts, red lipstick and powder. Laughter was echoing around when the bells went down. Sam tore off his wig, tucked his skirt inside his trousers and was off.

It was a chimney fire and when it was out, Sam was taking particulars. He was worried the way the old couple were giving him some old fashioned looks. When he was outside, the boys told him his skirt was hanging down his back. 'Oh no, not poofs in uniform,' he cried.

The New Year appeared dull and drab. There was little to cheer about at home, and the news abroad was grim. 'What the hell is going to happen? Where do we go from here?' were Ken Watson's predictably blunt questions put to John Lander. He did not know but was not happy in his bones. 'Hitler doesn't like his own medicine back,' said John. 'We are going to get a pasting some when, somewhere. It has got to happen.' That was his prophecy.

Raiders came and went away – if they escaped the guns and fighters! Then, Exeter was a special target! 'Hitler has flown into a rage after a big British raid on Lubeck. He threatens our cities will be eradicated one by one as reprisals.' Ken was telling Lucy, when reading his newspaper, he spotted that German papers were referring to Baedeker raids. The name was of the internationally famous guide-books to such famous landmarks. 'I guess Lubeck is in it.' 'Terror attacks?' Lucy cocked an ear, she did not say anything else, she knew what he meant.

But that was after the second city, Bath, was terrorised. It did not take long as the Luftwaffe pressed every plane possible into the attack. People living outside on the hills looked down on the swastika wings as they flew in with high explosives and incendiaries, machine-gunning as they went.

When the bombers came back the second night, there were more on the hills watching. The blase habit of staying in bed when the sirens sounded had gone. Everybody was alert again.

And, the NFS was on the road again. It was the same old story. Hundreds killed, double that number seriously hurt. Many fine buildings of both cities flattened or burnt down.

When Ken found time, he added extra detail to his diary. 'First raids were on Exeter, the fourth, the last, early on moonlit May 4, was the worst. Planes so low, machine-gunners having a go at firemen and all rescue workers. Again concentrated bombing, two-wave attack. HE and thousands of incendiaries and oil bombs, shopping areas in ruins. They say nearly 250 have been killed.

'Georgian Bath was hit two nights. April 25 and 26. Again the bombers came in very low, short and sharp, then back, re-loaded, within three hours. The next night, it was soon after midnight on the Sunday, 400-plus died. Old part of the city badly hit, including control centre. The weather seems deathly cold!'

The others that followed, Norwich, York, Canterbury, especially, were too far away to need their personal help. It was a case of thinking about the other blokes who he knew would be there – '14 Baedeker raids is final total, but the RAF is really knocking them down.' Then it was back to the more regular targets, Birmingham, Southampton, and so on.

*   *   *

What was tonight's raid going to be like? It was just a buzz around the main station that the Midlands seemed to be in trouble. Harold's pal, Lenny, vividly remembered soon after he joined full-time – he 'scraped in' at 16! – Coventry taking another heavy attack. It stood in his mind every time they headed in that direction.

Soon a convoy was called for. All pumps would be towed by the new ATVs, the very welcome two-ton vans. It would probably end up as Birmingham, although somebody was talking of Nuneaton?

Lenny, now 17, and a despatch rider at the main central station, would find the ATVs eased his task slightly as he kept them together, as they travelled through the night. They were on their way as the sirens sounded at home. Even his 350 Velocette seemed to purr more confidently.

It was a far cry from those short months ago when he was told his bicycle was not much good for his work. 'Take this motor cycle to Prospect Park headquarters, a DR will be there to tell you how to ride it,' was his instruction!

'How do I get it there,' thought Lenny. He persuaded a fireman to start it for him and sat on the saddle. Now was the moment to remember all those quiet back streets he had learnt so conscientiously as alternative routes. Today they were the main roads, as far as he was concerned. He set off, and made it.

Lenny was given an hour's training in the peaceful surroundings of the park roads. At the end, the instructor said, 'Good, now you are a despatch rider.' Back to his station he rode, and reported his new role.

By the time of this call, Lenny was used to convoy work. Often he led the way to Testwood and then, from the reinforcing station, on to Portsmouth, Southampton, and other South Coast targets. One night, starting from Testwood, he was stopped by police half-way to Plymouth; the convoy was not needed. Another, it was all the way into London.

Tonight he safely shepherded the ten pumps quickly brought together in Reading. Once in the streets of the nameless Midland cities, he still did not know where he was, but he did know he was still needed. He was asked to provide pillion transport for the controlling officer. Into the blazing streets they went, all strange to Lenny, it did not matter. The officer was telling him, 'Go this way, or Stop here,' as they moved from one trouble-spot to another. The bike was ideal for the officer, they could dodge the danger spots. Lenny was not so sure! Word was there were a lot dead, and phosphorous incendiaries were being used! But he survived another two days.

Heading south again, he was looking forward to going home to see Mum. He expected to be off duty when they reported in. The men could, but not Lenny. 'A column of 50 London pumps have to get home as well,' said the officer. 'You guide them as far as Maidenhead, then you can go home.'

There was no complaint from Lenny, as a teenager he thought all the action was wonderful.

*   *   *

Harold Randle was out of bed, instinctively, as the siren wailed. Helmet on he rode off on his cycle. His Scout friend in the ARP did as well, but he was not even half awake. He pedalled off, straight into a mini-roundabout. The kerb tipped him over

125

the handlebars, on to the earth top, and he rolled down the other side. He was so tired he was not hurt. Harold did not even stop.

As he reached the main road, Lenny passed. The convoy was close behind. Harold could not cross over so he watched. 'Eight, nine, ten,' he counted. 'I wonder where they are going?' He knew it was most likely the Midlands, they were on the main Oxford Road.

As soon as he could, Harold crossed the road to the bus shelter and stopped. Regularly, he met Linda, one of their station firewomen, and gave her a lift on his cycle's crossbar the three miles to U-station. Together they would clink steel helmets as he pedalled, ridiculous but it was appreciated – better than on foot. Tonight there was no sound of her coming. He rode on.

U-station's regulars had gone with the convoy, those left and the part-timers were quickly manning the other units. Harold stood quietly by. Apart from the miserable drone of German bombers all was quiet. Half-an-hour later a clatter of running feet, across the garage floor, undoubtedly a woman's. Into the room came Linda, gasping, it was a long way to hurry.

The siren had only half awakened her, but the time she got up and dressed, she had missed Harold. Dressed? Suddenly she realised that she had thrown on her top clothes but her camiknickers were clutched, for all to see, in her hands! Everybody laughed, it was a light relief on a bad night for other towns.

*   *   *

Such laughter was an antidote to the horrors. Audrey was hurrying to her turn of duty at another of the major stations. One of four sisters, all leaving home at the same time, she was on the bus when she realised that her panties were still airing! Meeting another firewoman, she whispered to her, and said, 'Cover for me, I must go back home.'

Finally reaching the fire station, Audrey found her 'friend' had duly reported the reason for her absence at roll call! Soon everyone knew.

Audrey was just off riding pillion to another town's station, when, before she could climb on, the DR asked a question. Not, 'Do you feel safe on the back?' but 'Are you all right today?' Then, in the middle of a serious all-night exercise, she was working in the mobilising van, when among all the paper messages 'Make pumps five ...', 'Mobile dam to ...', came one 'Firewoman Audrey, Reinforcements, pair of pants'.

Repeatedly she was to ask, 'Is nobody every going to let me live it down.' At least she could laugh.

*   *   *

Gradually, in the summer. attacks dwindled and Ken wrote, 'What a dreadful state abroad – everywhere. Now, at last, the Ministry of Home Security pleads with people to clear their lofts, to cut the risk of fires in raids.' Then, more cheerfully, he was able to add, 'Two raids in September, one in October, it seems to have stopped again.'

But, that Summer, Reading had had its own problems.

*   *   *

When the bells went down and the message spread 'Fire at Ministry of Food sugar store, Kentwood brick works,' everyone knew they were in for a nasty, potentially dangerous, night. Nationally, at any fire, above all the firemen's problems, there was always the desperate need to try and save whatever food stocks possible. Every half-a-pound sugar lost was a week's ration at the grocer's.

The slick NFS mobilising turned out the pumps and men in numbers. The new turntable ladder, pride and joy of Reading's Z-station, was on its way to its baptism of fire. Able to manoeuvre a fireman 80 to 100 feet above the ground, to direct his jet into the seat of flames, turntable ladders had proved vital in the blitzes. But, they were scarce before the war because of their cost, and mostly made in Germany!

An answer had been found, war-time Merryweather specials were built on Leyland bus chassis, with the intricate steel ladders engineered in Britain. Reading in 1942 had just received its first – GLW 420.

Now the Reading crew were clanging their bell as they hurried the huge 12-ton vehicle to the blaze. No need to ask the way, the sky was alight as the flames ripped through the roof. A dry old brick kiln, it was ideal as a temporary home for Tate and Lyle to pack sugar; with its previous use it also had the ingredients for the perfect inferno.

Harold's pal Lenny, as a full-time despatch rider, was there. It was his night. So much water was needed that the decision was made to pump from the River Thames, a mile or so away. Lenny was used to being 'sheep dog' to convoys of pumps heading for strange towns. Tonight, he knew this territory like the back of his hand.

Seven pumps he got into position, and then led the hose-laying lorry as it spewed its thousands of feet of endless lines of hose, to connect between the pumps, and then arrive in triumph at the fire. With the practised skill, it did not take long.

From then on Lenny spent his time keeping them in touch with each other, increasing or decreasing pressure to match the flow of water. At 17, on his motor-cycle, he felt king.

Flames roared up as the sugar fed the outbreak. The heat was intense, even more than expected by the new TL crew. The man detailed for the top work clambered the short distance to his platform, clipped himself on, and was raised into the air. A frightening world of his own, only in touch by intercom telephone. But he had a good pressure of water, thanks to Lenny and the relay.

It was a real stinker to fight. There was danger everywhere, regardless of the ever present thought, 'Would German planes spot it?'

An explosion rocked the building. Dust from the sugar in the air sparked it, and it flashed through the old building. Two guard dogs could not escape and, badly burnt, had to be destroyed. A task the otherwise hardened firemen hated.

The roaring fire flared higher, its searing heat intolerable. 'That man on the top of the turntable ladder, he's in real danger,' Lenny heard Gordon Castle's frantic cry.

In the same split second, the man at the top was crying out, 'Get me out!' The skin on his face and hands was burning off.

Even as his voice came over the intercom, the operator was instinctively swinging him out, and then bringing the ladder down. 'Ambulance,' he shouted, without waiting to see.

Roger Smith, recounting the story to Harold – disappointed because he missed the fire. He was in London of all places – said, 'We lost a lot of food, but there was nothing we could do once it spread.'

He laughed. 'There was a sticky problem afterwards. Everybody had so much sugar on their uniforms that the stations were plagued with wasps. You should have heard the girls up at the park.'

*   *   *

Since the National Fire Service had settled down the Luftwaffe seemed to have changed its tactics. 'Why?' asked Shorty as the men at U-station sat and planned for the next day. 'Everything is getting too hot for them,' said Roger Smith. 'The new fighters, the batteries of ack-ack guns, and the hundreds, thousands, of barrage balloons, but, mark my words, they will keep coming. At night, as well as these quick hit-and-run day raids.'

Shorty did not like Roger's uncanny knack of foretelling – especially trouble. 'These American day raids are niggling the Nazis,' he replied. 'Yes, but you see all the build up on the British dromes with these new four-engined planes. They carry far more bombs than the Yanks, and there are whispers of frequent thousand-plane night raids. That is really going to mean retaliation – and we shall be busy, mark my words.'

A silence followed for a moment as they sipped their tea. 'Come on let's prepare to help the war factory with its new heating,' said Roger.

The factory was ready to switch over to oil to fire the furnaces, it had erected an oil tank, and it needed to know whether there were any leaks before it poured in the oil. 'No one can afford to waste any, it's too precious,' grunted Roger. 'Well we can help them. Take two crews with large trailer pumps and fill the tank with water. Any leaks will spurt out and their electric welder can stop them immediately.'

What Roger had not told Shorty, as he found out the next morning, was that the pumps had to be manhandled over railway lines to the pumping site. And, when he got there, it was the outflow from the sewerage works! But all the hauling was worthwhile.

Slowly the level rose as it flooded the huge cavern. Then, as it reached half-full, calamity. The float operating the outside indicator slipped from its pulley, and dropped into the bottom of the tank. 'Oh no,' thought Shorty, 'not in there.' But it was one of the factory workmen who readily stripped off and lowered himself through the inspection manhole. 'Aptly named,' brooded Roger as he watched with great concern.

Three times the man dived to the bottom of the tank, and, then, up he came with the float in his hand, cheers echoed; to all of them he was a real hero. 'It takes guts to

128

jump through a manhole and do that. Well done,' said Shorty shaking his hand, as he was pulled out.

The float was refixed and the pumping started again. When the job was done just three pin pricks were found. 'Now we have to empty it,' Shorty told his men. But it was worth it. The works' boss said to Shorty. 'Your firemen have had a long hard day. Dinner is laid on for them in the works' canteen.' That was a treat – and something to brag about when they returned to the station in the early evening.

*   *   *

Not everything in the way of special services can be planned. Gordon's phone rang as he sat in his office one evening. An agitated superintendent from the hospital asked, 'Can you help? The water supply in the hospital has failed – the overhead tank is bone dry!'

Clearly this was an emergency. Gordon put the bells down – 'It will get the men's adrenalin running after two nights again without a siren,' he thought, and smiled. The problem soon became apparent. Opening the hydrant in the hospital grounds, the water just trickled out. On the main road the result was just the same. Low pressure and the hard-at-work factories drawing off extra water had created a hidden crisis.

Why and how? was a problem for the water company. 'Go back to the trunk main,' Gordon told his men. 'Run hose all the way, up the fire escape and over the roof, and then into the tank. Fill it that way but, you must use new hose, we cannot risk contamination.'

He smiled to himself as he remembered the spaghetti coils of used hose tangled, and frozen solid, in the streets of places like Bristol. Times were certainly changing.

*   *   *

Fog was another curse of the blackout. It was widespread and thick when the divisional headquarters' men and women changed duty. Stories of difficulty in reaching the mansion in the middle of the park were being relayed by the oncoming watch who had struggled in. There were hopes of a quiet night. 'Let's hope it's the same over France,' said the control officer. 'It will keep the bombers on the ground.'

Peter, always the gentleman, volunteered to guide the two firewomen, out of the park. They struggled their way through the smelly murk, lost the path and suddenly found something tall appear right in front of them. They laughed as they realised how stupid it all was. It was a tree but, as they found another, they realised that somehow they had crossed to the other side of the park.

Finally reaching the main gate, they could hear the noises of shouting and a heavy engine revving. Firemen with strong torches reduced to matchlights were trying to guide a low-loader into the park. 'Turn round girls, and go back. You will be lost if you go any further,' they said.

129

The two girls said 'No, we want to reach our billets in Brunswick Street.' Crossing the road, they kept their hands on the wall and followed it. It was a good idea but it did not lead home. Eventually, they found they had walked all the way to the main Oxford Road. It was a long detour.

There was much frustration in travelling. Eight inches of snow faced a Datchet fireman as he left home two hours early to trudge to his duty on Slough's trading estate. 'I knew I had to get there,' he said. Another day, when off duty, he cycled backwards and forwards five times, five miles each way, as the sirens repeatedly sounded.

*   *   *

Duty hours at the mansion were the same as at fire stations. And, just the same, each time the siren sounded it was back to control, on duty. The woman officer, Pam, living in a house on the fringe of the park – the road leading to the ordnance factory – faced a good half-a-mile to run. Nearby was another firewoman, Jill. At the first rising note of the siren it was instinct for both to jump out of bed, pull on slacks and tunic, and start the trudge.

But not this night. Jill was so exhausted that she slept oblivious of the horrible banshee noise. It was the battering on her front door, rattling of the letter box, that broke into her sleep. Her hair was in curlers but there was nothing she could do about that.

Pulling on her steel helmet to cover them, together they set off for the park. Pitch black, it was winter, they ran straight into the net of a football pitch, collapsing entangled in the mud of the goalmouth. Caught like rabbits by a poacher, they cursed Hitler as struggling to find their way out of the net, they knew they still had to run up the steep hill to the house.

Jill was shrieking, 'All those men are going to see me in these hair curlers!'

'The original owner of the park must have been a drunkard,' said a fireman, after hearing the explanation from the dirtied and dishevelled firewomen.

'If I go over to the George and Dragon for a pint, I line those trees up in groups of four on the way back. I say "Hello Four", and it brings me to the footpath by the bowling green and straight to the house.'

There was quiet laughter and everyone moved off to their tasks. All were always ready for the adrenalin to run if the German bombers came their way.

'It's a good night for the ghost?' said one fellow in a croaking voice. 'It's not true,' responded Jill, refusing to be hassled any more. 'What I hate are the bats hanging up in the corridors.'

It was a scary place for anyone with frayed nerves, for whatever reason. No lino on the floors, the bare boards created their own ominous noises as people hurried over them. And, quite definite rat lines. Especially, their trails could be traced along the passages by the girls' quarters

Broken down and deserted until pressed into service by the NFS, it was definitely not a place for the visitors who would have enjoyed its Georgian glory.

*   *   *

Although on first call, Harold was sent to the fish and chip shop. It had some fish. It was a filthy foggy night, but the news had spread fast and there was a queue. 'Hurry,' he kept saying to himself. Finally, his turn. Collecting his newspaper packets, he came out through the blackout canvas door into the thick murk.

He could not see an inch but he tried to run, he knew the way. Thump, he was stopped by a big immovable object, which should not have been there! He had run straight into a policeman. Apologising, he set off again, straight into a trolleybus pole. Harold walked the rest of the way. 'If there is a fire, it will be another of those endless chimney fires,' he tried to tell himself.

*   *   *

Another important Service establishment watched over by the Windsor firemen was an OCTU. It was coping with 300-strong courses for the ATS, training them to be officers. At the end of the two-months hard studying they relaxed with a final dance. Firemen were among the outsiders invited in to provide partners.

Arriving with a major pump – no sophistication, they were still ready for a call – they joined in. A 'Paul Jones', all circulated the floor and took new dancers. Charles Walin, who in charge of the crew, found his new partner friendly and talkative. So, making conversation, he said, 'There is a rumour that Mary Churchill, daughter of the Prime Minister, is on this course. Is it true?' 'Oh, it's more than a rumour, it's definitely true,' she laughed. 'I know, I am Mary Churchill.'

Charles was to keep her in his mind and remember that night, when she married and became a lady-in-waiting to the Queen.

19 · Arms and Invasion

Quite suddenly the main streets everywhere in 1942 were becoming busy. From the few 'very essential' cars and lorries of 1940–41, times were changing. Our own fighting services were gearing up; so, too, our own re-organised fire service – part-timers were ordered they could no longer resign. It all needed transport, mobility, in a way never understood in Britain before.

Overnight, it seemed, the Americans had arrived. Their tough, mass-produced, lorries, with big, rough terrain tyres and rear wheels one behind the other, were so strange. Especially the nearside steering wheel. Yet, in no time, they were so commonplace.

So too, the ubiquitous Jeep – no doors, windows, and only a canvas cover to defeat the British rain – with its relaxed, lounging we might say, chewing drivers, pointing it down the 'wrong side of the road'. In smart olive green uniforms, it was the start of an 'arms and armed invasion' of Britain.

On duty they were gun happy, off duty they came to see the strange British institutions. Who could have foreseen, in 1943 and 44, such crowded dances for their jitterbugging in the town's Victorian town hall. Glenn Miller, Squadron-naires, all the big bands playing enthusiastically.

Who could have realised they would be so friendly – yet, seemed so strange to us?

*   *   *

The common lands from Aldermaston to Highclere, and in many other directions, were transformed as the Americans set up camps and aerodromes. For the NFS there was a lot of liaison to be given. These new combatants had little idea of living under the shadow of enemy bombers.

Gordon Castle met a group to advise on water supplies, as they pulled in one morning, virtually self-contained with their equipment. Confidently the US officer looked at a dirty green pond and said, 'Don't worry, that will be drinking water by tonight, after we have finished treating it.'

There was the same off-duty friendly optimism, at every half-chance, as Liz's friend, Angie, found when her Blue watch was on duty at the Park. An American base operator telephoned to talk with an officer. Quick as a flash, when the business call was over, he rang back. 'How about you girls meeting us at the Ship Hotel, in Reading, tonight?' She looked at the other two girls, and repeated the question. In unison, they said 'Yes.'

They had a good evening chatting and laughing, two different cultures mixing easily. It was something the whole area was to get well-used to. But the war was still going on and it was back to the Park. They were both on duty again that night.

Ken Watson met with downright point-of-the-gun resistance when he was turned out because of a huge bonfire breaking the blackout. Loaded rifles met him. No way were these coloured Americans going to put out such a lovely fire. They were cold! It took their own commanding officer, with gun strapped to his hip, to dress them down. Their determined looks turned to huge broad grins – they could not understand all the fuss.

*   *   *

There were also gun-happy Home Guards in Reading and around the country. It was a chance to shoot back. They manned a Z-rocket battery at Whiteknights, firing the new projectiles. Home Guards took over many ack-ack sites and Z-batteries as ground defences strengthened.

*   *   *

As the camps and airfields multiplied so too did the danger from the Luftwaffe's concentration on daylight fighter-bomber raids. Fewer planes but maximum harassment: usually in pairs, or fours, up to ten strikes a day. Cloudy days were the biggest risk, as they raced to beat the British fighters and hit our airfields – and special targets.

As Reading worried about its sugar, Bristol suffered badly from a one-plane raider. No siren, and a bomb hit the centre. 'Three buses, double-deckers, wiped out. I hear 48 died,' wrote Ken Watson, beginning to wonder just where his diary was going to end.

'What does one do to counter such dreadful attacks?' Ken asked John Lander. Shaking his head, John said, 'Not much. the fighters are knocking them down, but now they are coming with their own fighter escorts, some are bound to get through. Still one is less a danger than hundreds pouring down bombs.'

It was a practical answer but not one to give much comfort to those attacked. John was to remember that in a few months in Reading!

Sooner than that, though, Canterbury was to feel the weight of 60–70 attackers, flying in low, with as many fighters to protect them. And some more came back at night.

Then, came the news of the Anglo-American invasion of North Africa. 'People can cheer, but the really good news is it must take away more of the Luftwaffe,' said Ken. He was right, there were no more heavy raids in 1942.

But that was not the only important switch. Ken was on the move to take over a main station and controlling outlying stations, in Buckinghamshire. The NFS had made its assessments and officers had, or were, taking on their new roles.

Church bells were soon ringing too – 'First time since 1940. What a strange feeling, it's no longer means an invasion,' Roger Smith said to Harold as they stood listening. 'Mark this day, Sunday, November 15, we are celebrating. And the country has dedicated it as Civil Defence Day. The Home Front fighters are recognised.' He stopped, feeling he had involuntarily made a speech. 'What was it said when it was announced? "To remember those other days when Civil Defenders did so much to keep our will to win invincible".' Churchill, wasn't it?

'I hope some of our boys are going on the blitz veterans parade with the King taking the salute. Dover and Coventry are going to lead.'

*   *   *

'The war is changing,' said Ken as he read through a new set or orders. 'Something is bound to happen soon. Everything points to it.' In his hands were instructions for 'Exercise Harlequin'. Tim Price, No 2 at his new Bucks station when he arrived, was with him.

'Tim, the NFS is going to exercise its capability to move a lot of firemen from the North down to the South of England, to reinforce us.' Lifting his eyes in puzzlement, Tim didn't reply. 'We are going to have the men, women and machines, ready to protect all the forces we know are around.'

'Do you think it's the real thing?' asked Tim. 'Some of us think it could be but I don't know, it makes sense to try it out first,' replied Ken.

There was a lot to be done. Firemen and women coming from the north were very ready to play their part. Had not the last heavy German raids been on Merseyside and other northern industrial towns? Some were absorbed into Ken's and all the other regular stations. Others manned part-time stations, which normally would only be operational at night, when the firemen came home from their work.

One of the urgent tasks listed was to ensure that all static water supplies 'on certain roads' were plotted and marked. 'Routes for the invasion convoys?' whispered Ken to Tim. 'I wonder.' The instruction was quite precise, it even listed the need to mark supplies up to certain distance off the roads.

Here the fun commenced, ponds shown on the ordnance maps were dried up because of the abnormally dry weather. Men were sent out to erect special boards to indicate the sources, the approximate gallonage, and distance from the road. The men might be strangers but they were all operational firemen, and Ken had no qualms of water being plotted which was choked with weeds or unapproachable by a fire pump.

'The information will stand them in good stead,' noted Ken. Adding, with his usual wryness, 'Provided the powers-that-be don't transfer them to another district when they come back!'

Tim laughed and said, 'Well at least they have found some ponds that even we never suspected.' 'Yes, so did some part-time action station men,' laughed Ken.

'We have also learnt some new Northern expressions about fire-fighting in the countryside.' 'Yes, running out 1,200 feet of hose across ploughed fields to a fire isn't what they are used to – they obviously find it different to roads and pavements!' replied Tim.

While the preparations for Europe's invasion were getting under way, Ken's men received an urgent request for help – one that was going to make them use a few good Southern words.

A Highland Division stationed nearby wanted water pumped from the lake in the grounds of the house where they were billeted, into a large, wide trench. Ken sent his men immediately. The smell from the lake could be sensed even before they started pumping, and the men weren't sorry when the job was done.

Back at the station, suctions and pumps were all washed out and cleaned, and hose scrubbed and hung up to dry, before they could stand easy for their overdue cup of tea.

There were shouts of anguish when, in the afternoon, the Highland Division's officer asked them to come back and empty the trench. 'Ten thousand gallons of water, what are they mucking about at?' protested Tim. 'I don't know but they clearly think it is important,' responded Ken.

Off went the crews and it was scrub out and clean down again, after an energetic afternoon. Early next day, the Army asked for urgent help again. Not once but twice. 'What the hell's happening,' was the general sense of the grunts and profanities as the firemen pumped the smelly water from the lake to the trench and back – and then did it all over again. It was a long, hard, and dirty day, more so because no Scottish voice was answering any questions.

When the call came on the third day, Ken quietly went along himself – just to keep his eyes and ears open. It was a wide trench and was to be used as a testing trial for the waterproofing of various types of armoured vehicles that were to be used on D-Day.

The first attempts had not been successful because the bottom was too soft and the vehicles bogged down. So it was emptied and bricks laid, until the soldiers got it right so the vital work could proceed. When this was explained to the firemen they were quite bucked to have been able to take part.

*   *   *

There was clearly more news about London by the way Tom Goldsmid dashed to see John Lander in the Caversham station. Christmas festivities and, more important the quiet time, were clearly to be swept away as forgotten memories. London had suffered its heaviest night attack for 18 months – he had already heard that there were something like 40 unexploded bombs handicapping the firemen who were working there.

Now, three days later, a daylight attack had caught the city completely by surprise. Tom was full of it. 'The barrage balloons were down; the siren was too late, and they've hit a school in Lewisham before anyone could take shelter. A lot of children are dead.'

John felt as sorry as Tom but, also, he felt so helpless, sitting there. Life was busy enough now that Ken had gone, the station always seemed to be on the boil answering fire calls which had nothing to do with the Germans.

'That's tough,' he replied. 'I know how you feel but all we can do is keep on top line, you never know when it might be us.'

20 · Death strikes home

The German plane streaked down the River Kennet valley towards Reading. Section Leader Henry Barnes sensed it; he looked up from his desk and through a window of the Mansion House, across the 'peaceful' countryside. Appointed finance officer, he was working on intricate figures but the feeling was enough.

He stood up, took off his glasses, to believe what he could see. At the same moment a senior company officer passing on the patio below, shouted. 'Look, a Jerry fighter-bomber!' It all happened as if in slow motion. In seconds the ugly dark shape, with its black crosses, was gone from sight.

Harold Randle had just left his girl friend at her solicitors' office, walked along Friar Street and round the corner to his newspaper's office, in Valpy Street. Passing the Town Hall and Queen Victoria's statue, he noted, for the first time, how the Queen had her back to the town, looking at the nearby railway station, giving the impression of not wanting to ever see the town again.

He had been to fix a date. Walt Disney's Bambi was on at the Central; the 'Technicolor masterpiece' The Great Mr Handel at the Vaudeville; and, on stage, at the Palace Theatre, it was Wee Georgie Wood with Dolly Harmer heading a variety bill. There was a good choice with nine cinemas in the town.

On a February afternoon it would soon be dark and he dare not be away long from the office. In 1943 Harold was a very junior reporter on the Reading Standard. He had been there four weeks.

Hardly had he slipped in the side door, and up to the tiny editorial office, just below the roof, than all hell was let loose. Crump, crump, crump, crump, came the echoing noise of a stick of bombs. At the same time a plane swept at nil feet over the rooftop, firing its machine guns all the way across the railway station and into Caversham. Together the journalists dived to the floor.

As they did the floorboards seem to come up to meet them, the whole building shook, and there were bullet holes in the roof! The unexpected was as much a shock as the attack. Dazed, everybody stood still as they rose, expecting more. Generations of dust gave the whole thing an eerie scenario.

Suddenly everybody was talking. Compositors in the typesetting room below could be heard, and, strangely, through the wall, the people in the rival Berkshire Chronicle next door. Immediate thought of Harold was that he had not brought his steel helmet – he had not wanted to create an impression as a new, very junior, boy. Dashing down the stairs, he found nobody wounded, only shocked.

Back upstairs, he said to Joan, a couple of years older than himself, 'I must go, I'm in the Fire Service.' With that cryptic message, he ran out.

As he reached the street door, he stood undercover for a moment. Lethal stalactites of window glass were still falling, creating a cacophony of almost musical sound. Glass was everywhere. The front office staff had been unbelievably fortunate. Only the back-boards to the window display had kept the slivers of the big plate glass window from them.

The street was a sea of glass and odd pieces of masonry. Harold ran round the corner, back the way he had come only minutes before. A ghastly sight met him. The other side of the Town Hall was wrecked, so was the front of St Laurence's, the civic church. In between there was a large hole, Blandy and Blandy another firm of solicitors had received the last of the stick of four bombs.

Fire was flaring up in the wreckage. Queen Victoria still stood unmoved. At the same moment up came a mobile dam unit. There was no crew; the driver was a part-time officer who had run from his work at the Thames Conservancy to the main fire station, grabbed the fire engine and brought it to the bombing.

Harold ran to the pump, there was work to be done. He did spare a thought for his office clothes, several in fact, because of the clothes rationing coupons, then got on with the job.

'My God,' he suddenly remembered, 'the town's ARP control room is down under that corner of the town hall!'

Reinforcements for all the Civil Defence services arrived, masses of them. The walking wounded were bandaged and hurried away, the Rescue men were digging in the wreckage searching for a solicitor and staff. It looked very bad for some. The fire was controlled, escaping gas had started it.

But that last bomb had cut the electricity and telephone cables to the town's Civil Defence Report Centre. 'It was a Dornier Do 217. I could see two people in it,' gabbled one of the men tugging at the wreckage. 'It was flying so low I could see the man firing the machine gun. A bullet went through the plate glass window where I was working.' Others were arguing that it was a Messerschmitt 110, but did it matter, in that one swift hit-and-run raid, the Luftwaffe had managed to disrupt the nerve-centre of the town's carefully practised rescue operations. And there was still one or more people trapped, possibly dead, in that bomb's wreckage.

It was only then that word of the enormity of the disaster reached Harold. The first of the stick of bombs slammed into the back of Simond's brewery, and into Yield Hall Lane; the next, in Minster Street, wiped out most of Wellsteed's department store, and the back of Heelas' store was also rubble. Both were shut because it was early closing day. But, the third had hit the People's Pantry, in the Arcade – and this popular 'British restaurant' was packed!

It seemed more important to be there. There was clearly work to do.

*   *   *

Hours later, Harold collected his cycle and rode home. It was like a wake when he walked in. Mother, father, and girl friend, all huddled silently round the fire. Nobody spoke for a moment – the last they knew he was walking past the spot where the bombs dropped, and then he had disappeared!

All Harold wanted to do was be sick, not just the carnage but the stench of the coal gas, in which all had been working, had got to him at last. Where to go that evening had resolved itself.

*   *   *

Gordon Castle was standing outside W-station when he heard the whoof of the bombs echoing across the town. He could see the debris going up into the air. 'That's Huntley and Palmers,' he thought aloud. Then turning, he shouted,'Turn out.' As the men came running, he said, 'Don't wait for the call, we are going now.'

In the lead machine, he reached King's Road and still had not found anything. Then he could see the fire in Minster Street and headed for that. There was a hell of a mess at the back of the two departmental stores. Blakes, the sports shop was burning well, it had crumpled as the first bomb landed in Yield Hall Lane and went on into Heelas' garages, wrecking the firm's hearses.

Gordon ordered his driver over the rubble and headed for the fire, where they got to work. A man had died in that first mess, also two children in Minster Street on their way home from school. Like Harold, Gordon had no idea that the People's Pantry had been hit in the picturesque and historic Arcade, a hundred yards away off Broad Street.

A column officer, a Londoner who had seen much in the city's 1940 blitz, came over as the fire was controlled. 'You had better bring your crew round and help get out some of those trapped in the People's Pantry.'

It was a scene of desolation beneath the shattered glass dome of the restaurant – a popular place for a cup of tea to escape the cold on a bleak winter's day, even if there was little to eat. Then Gordon was told about the further disaster at the Town Hall, just a further hundred yards away. There was no way of getting through to see, there was no time anyhow.

'Come on' said Gordon. 'This is going to be nasty.' His men grunted and followed. Sprinklers and alarms were going off everywhere, glass was still a major danger as they crunched over it while bits continued to fall. Windows were blown out and, like store signs, were hanging precariously.

Harold, from his pump, had been keeping a special eye on the sign over the Arcade Chambers, almost drunkenly clinging by a thread above its Friar Street entrance, just yards from the town hall bomb.

Fortunately, the high-explosive bombs meant no major fires. Leaking, stinking, gas was the major worry. But everyone just got on with the job. Gordon and his men systematically set to, searching the roofs of the many buildings making up the arcade and adjoining Market Place, looking for survivors, or bodies, thrown by the blast. It was nasty, brick dust, glistening glass and amid the debris, flesh.

Another crew, who were out building a concrete emergency dam, were quick to get to Wellsteeds. 'We were burrowing underneath, salvaging emergency rations for the town which were stored there,' they told Gordon afterwards. 'The Heavy Rescue boss asked us to help, his reinforcing teams were still on the way from other towns. The American troops who raced into the town, came and gave us a hand as well.' That was typical of them, they had become part of the scene and wasted no time in arriving, ready to help.

'Good,' said Gordon, 'Do you realise its probably the first time most have seen devastation like this.'

*   *   *

Without any fuss, the Salvation Army appeared at the edge of the devastation in Minster Street, the nearest spot to their own headquarters. They came simply, with a table and an urn. They cleared enough rubble to make it stand steady, and started pouring.

It was like a prayer being answered, there was so much dust and coal gas in the atmosphere. So quickly and so simply. No everyday questions, like, 'What about your coupons?', everybody had the same word, 'Thanks.'

*   *   *

Desperation hit Ken Watson as he hurried back to his own station in Buckingham-shire and learned that Reading had been hit. It had been a bad, mundane day, already. The Home Office representative responsible to see that all firemen undertook physical training to ensure they were fit, had been touring the divisions with Ken. He wanted to know why it was the last place in the country to do regular PT?

Ken had been baulked all along the line, since becoming the officer responsible, after he came back from the training course. When the Home Office man asked bluntly, 'Why?' he told him. Clearly that was not going to be good news for the outspoken Ken, when it echoed through the system!

Suddenly it had become unimportant. After leaving Oxford the sirens sounded. 'What do you wish to do, sir? Carry on back to Aylesbury, or turn back?'

'Carry on,' he said. So Ken drove towards Aylesbury. In the distance ahead he saw a fire engine racing towards him at a flat-out pace. It was one from his own station. As it flashed-by its bell was clattering incessantly, as if to tell him something big was up! Beside the driver was Tim, and it was he who was shaking the bell rope.

Clearly his crew had no intention of stopping to give him the news – 'If only we had radio, like they're getting in the Army,' Ken thought to himself – so he put his foot down and went as fast as he could.

'What's up?' he asked as he ran from his car into the control room. 'Reading's been hit! So has Newbury! Mobilising asked for a pump to go to Newbury, Tim has taken a crew.'

Knowing Ken's home was in Reading, the rest added what else they had heard. 'Simonds brewery has gone up, so has Huntley and Palmers, the town hall has been hit.' They gave him all the lurid rumours.

It seemed that Reading was on the Luftwaffe's map. Cheeky, devastating, air attacks, penetrating right through to the middle of Southern England, at a time

140

when these had lessened! Going into his own office, he picked up the telephone and rang his divisional officer. 'Please sir, can I go to Reading? My wife and family are down there, and I would like to see what is happening?' 'No, stay at your post,' was the unequivocal response.

After all Ken had seen elsewhere, his mind was picturing acres of flattened debris. This time he was doing the worrying, instead of his wife.

Within minutes, the control room phone rang again. The firewoman shouted loudly, so that she knew Ken could hear, as she relayed the message, 'Stand down for Reading.' As soon as she replaced the receiver, she added the unofficial addition to the call, 'They have only had a stick of bombs, but everyone's gone mad!' She also noted, 'Tim says no major fires to deal with in Newbury.' Both messages were true, but badly under estimated the death and destruction just two planes had caused.

Ken was heading for home as soon as possible. Questions were still being debated at the fire station as to why the message 'Make pumps ten' had been made sent by an officer early on the spot. When Ken reached the People's Pantry and saw the devastation those four bombs had caused, he could understand.

There might not have been many fires, thank God, but clearly men with the guts and determination of their fire-fighters were needed to help with the rescue and recovery of so many bodies. As yet no-one knew the death toll: it seemed incredible that so many could escape because the shops were closed but, desperately sad that it should explode in a crowded restaurant.

The picture was far from clear, but there were many dead and many more seriously injured. And still quite a lot missing, unlike Harold Randle's return – including some from that very street where he had walked!

*   *   *

Tim Price's dash was also to find death and destruction. The raider, another Dornier, came out of the cloud over Newbury and, flying at roof top height just like at Reading, dropped its bombs. Machine-gunning the streets as it went. Fifteen people died, including school children and several people over 80.

Five were dead in the town's Senior Council School – a teacher saw the bomb come through the roof and go obliquely across the hall before exploding. 'There was a deafening bang and a vivid flash of light' – she lived to tell of the terror. Others were in nearby St Bartholomew's almshouses. St John's Church was demolished and a first-aid post put out of action.

Graphic stories were told to Tim as he arrived with his back-up firemen. The local Civil Defence services were already well under control – again, the HE bombs had meant no serious fires – and the work of digging went ahead. The Americans living in the camps around, again, lost no time in hurrying to help with the rescue work.

Most of the pupils had gone home. 'Thank God for that,' said Tim, as he listened. The headmaster was talking with his education secretary; in the staff room, at the other end of the building, were his wife, a teacher, PT instructor and 14-year-old Maurice, being coached for the Royal Navy.

All had miraculous escapes. After seeing the bomb arriving, the teacher felt herself whirled upside down, landing 15 feet down the stairs, surrounded by bricks and masonry. Maurice also had to be rescued from the debris. The headmaster's wife was unconscious.

In a classroom, a council carpenter was mending a lock, another pupil was watching him work. Both died. Nearby was the school's caretaker. He escaped but, his wife in the girls' school below was killed. So too were two of three girls who stayed behind to hang pictures on a classroom wall. Others typing, with teachers, were saved by specially-built blast walls.

*   *   *

By a quirk a senior divisional officer from Reading was studying at the Fire Services' college, at the Ocean Hotel, Saltdean, near Brighton. He saw the ack-ack guns bring down the Dornier, which had bombed Newbury. It was minutes too early to have been the Reading raider, that was hit by ack ack fire from the airfield at Tangmere. All eight of the two crews were killed, the planes breaking up as they crashed.

*   *   *

Censored newspaper reports said in precis, 'Dorniers operated in cloudy weather. Only two penetrated any distance, each caused damage to different towns in the Home Counties. Two shot down.' There was confusion over the death toll in Reading: 43 were reported dead – 39 in the People's Pantry – and 153 injured, 49 seriously. There were others who went home to see to their wounds.

That day raiders killed 77, with 123 seriously hurt, in three counties. It was a stark reminder that the war was far from over.

*   *   *

Clearly the NFS, and the other Civil Defence services, were ready to fight back if the Nazis hit heavily again but, in reality, the British bombers were now punishing them. The Russian front was taking most of their aircraft and, those left on the Western occupied countries were finding the best way to disturb Britain's war efforts, were these hit-and-run raids.

People in the two towns wanted to hit back: but none knew that 1,000-bomber raids were to return the devastation within days.

*   *   *

Sixteen days later, the NFS men were looking their smartest once more. They were on parade in Oxford, with other Civil Defence and youth organisations, celebrating

142

the 25th anniversary of the Red Army. It was the time of Mrs Clementine Churchill's Aid To Russia appeal, which was bringing in a good response.

Firemen like all the Civil Defence services were used to showing the flag to stimulate public support for a multitude of causes: War Weapons Week, Salute the Soldier, Wings for Victory, just to name a few.

*   *   *

As the devastation continued in so many famous towns, the Fire Force Commander was working hard to protect historic as well and war-vital buildings. He told a top-level briefing, 'Plans have been laid to protect special areas. If Oxford, Eton, and Windsor, were destroyed, buildings that can never be replaced would be lost. A list of high architectural value buildings and monuments has been drawn up.' He was quick to add, 'Similar precautions have been taken to deal with fires in places where industrial risks are high.'

It was strange how Oxford had escaped, apart from one go at the Nuffield works. But, Commander Taylor was not thinking of his three counties alone. As an example, he noted, 'We have given assistance in nearly every blitzed town. Seventy pumps were sent to Coventry on one occasion in 1942.' That showed how the NFS had changed the value of the fire-fighters.

*   *   *

In June, the whole of the NFS southern region took part in competitions at Hills Meadows, Reading. It was an early birthday – the second anniversary of the NFS was August 18. A Saturday spectacular, it was something to cheer people, also to show the efficiency of its men and women, and the equipment. Something that would have been far too risky, even if possible, two years before.

There were special cheers for the women with their physical training displays and prowess when competing in the pump drills. They proved they could knock down the targets with the water jets in record time. But they were never allowed to man pumps to fight fires.

It was a fascinating day, Harold Randle was extremely busy but thoroughly enjoying himself. So was Mr H M Smith, the Chief Regional Fire Officer. A March of Time portrayed fire fighters since the 17th Century; a display of today's training to show how men were kept keyed up, then the competitions.

Southampton, who had suffered so much, were best with the heavy pump, with neighbours Ringwood, for the part-timers. Teams from each region laid 300 feet of 6 inch steel piping – the winner in 4 minutes 31 seconds.

In the firewomen's fitness training, the home team were second. To tell the NFS world, pigeons were released to take the news back to the regions – they were still ready should all other communications fail.

It was capped with a 'fire', bringing in Fire Guard parties with their stirrup pumps, five pumps, the turntable ladder, a hose-laying lorry, and the 'fire control'.

Playing a prominent role in the display, alongside all this equipment, plus the

143

scaffolding dam and water unit, was the 'control unit', and field telephone van. Introduced by the Fire Force communications officer in 1942, the field telephone van was the pride and joy of Harold Randle and other messengers. Led by Leading Fireman 'Sibby' Beeson, they could create telephone links with considerable skill – and at some risk, as they performed balancing acts to hang the cables out of the way.

Set up as part of the big NFS plan to ensure good communications, it was equipped with miles of telephone wire, linesmen's equipment, and Army-type portable telephones. The FTV also proved most useful for public events. Especially this year's Wings for Victory, and all the other savings Weeks, which provided the public with some entertainment and collected money for the war effort. That year the NFS campaign for Wings for Victory had raised £54,600, when the target was £10,000. Clearly, firemen were appreciated now.

Harold wore two red 'corporal' stripes on his tunic and steel helmet. He was now senior messenger of Fire Force 15 and, with four leading messengers, with one stripe, he was expected to keep the messengers working together as a unit. 'And I am still not 17,' he muttered to himself when promoted.

His hand-written pocket book of knowledge he spent many hours passing on to others. It contained important facts about the FTV. Few 'grown-ups' could demand of the GPO operator a 'Private uninterrupted type call' – a 'PUT', it read. It meant an operator could connect him to vital control points in the fire service echelon, and would keep the line open as long as needed. Apart from his work as a messenger, it was a vital way of linking his field telephone system from a call box.

All messengers knew how to use the Police call boxes, 'Speak into the microphone and the operator will relay the message to fire sub-division control.' If they would not work, ask a policeman to unlock his box and the Police operator will put you straight through to control using their private wire.'

Everyone was thoroughly briefed on what to do if the Reading telephone exchange was blitzed. The nearest telephones on other exchanges were listed. Shepherd's House Hill, Calcot, and so on – No 5 Mayfield Cottage was the nearest for the Theale exchange, for example.

Then there were the 'last resorts', the telegraph office on the corner of Blagrave Street; or a reminder that the railways' telephone system worked independently. 'Fire Force Headquarters has arranged for messengers to be at Maidenhead station to collect messages if GPO telephones are blitzed.'

Just to complete the preparations, 'If the Maidenhead exchange is not working, phone Burnham 93. This comes up on Burnham exchange and they have a private wire to FFHQ.'

There was a lot to learn and teach, quite different from Len Hall's, 'You're a firemen first...'

Flicking other pages, Harold could list the three reinforcing bases if Reading was hit, Palmer Park, Prospect Park, and Bearwood School, and 51 spots where 'strangers' could be shown to pump and relay from Reading's natural waterways. There were also two sheets of other natural supplies, plus all the artificial sources, both over and under 50,000 gallons, right up to the 3,000,000 gallons in the town's reservoir on Bath Road.

It was packed with useful information, including the steel helmet and shoulder rankings for the NFS men and women, but not the stripes for the messengers!

*   *   *

When the Fire Force Commander summarised the pace of progress in the two years of the National Fire Service, the newspapers were quick to spot some good news. Excluding enemy action, the new force – it covered 2,250 square miles – dealt with 1,520 fire and special services calls in 1942. There were 1,067 men and 481 women full-time, and 3,741 men and 818 women part-time. It was 7,000 when it started.

'Volunteers outnumber paid men and women by five to one; if works brigades are included, it is 6½ to 1. The big factor in the Fire Force is the volunteer spirit.' Many he went on were doing more than their compulsory 48 hours duty.

Paying tribute to the women, he said, they were employed as telephone operators, drivers, despatch riders, cooks, and in administration. 'None were engaged on fire fighting.'

In the Fire Force there were 476 pumps, 612 appliances and two turntable ladders. He added, 'The force had a special savings drive and raised the cost of the TLs' ladders, £9,500.'

Three fire stations, out of six, had been built, and 84 adapted, with the work done by the NFS. Firemen had also surveyed 1,500 sites where they could pump water from rivers and streams, built over 400 static water tanks, there was a programme going forward for 250 tanks and 18 miles of the steel pipelines, again, all being carried out by the NFS.

Commander Taylor casually dismissed as 'unusual' 1,600 phosphorous bombs in a fire which took ten days to put out. In contrast he paid tribute to the 'spare-time war production work, such as rubber plugs for airmen's masks. Also, 'the hundreds of toys' – for the force maintained a number of war-time nurseries.

'No fireman gained directly from the money earned. Half went to the Government and the remainder to central welfare funds.'

Harold chuckled when he heard the 'FFC' say that. 'We spent hours last winter making snow shoes for the Russians. It was mucky, threading that waxed string through the wooden rounds and trying to fix the cross-over thongs.'

*   *   *

As the American troops flooded into Southern England they were quick in making close contact with the NFS. The 'Yanks', an affectionate if not necessarily accurate description, were a cultural shock to the traditionalists. Unaffected by years of clinging on to survive as a country with everything in short supply, they came buoyant and confident; they were the tops.

'Good,' said Ken Watson when discussing the first visit from US troops encamped on their patch. Such discussions, undoubtedly, were taking place in

145

many other stations. 'We need a boost, but sometimes they really do need taking down a peg.'

It did not take long. Ken went to one of the aerodromes, where the Americans were operating. His mission to arrange an exercise so that the two countries' fire fighters could learn to work together – speed and understanding being so urgent when coping with plane crashes.

One US officer, keen to show that he had been studying, asked about the Home Office diffusers. This vital branch nozzle which, with its spinner could produce a sheet of spray, to envelope flames, cut off oxygen, and choke out a fire, had been a masterpiece supplied with the war-time equipment. It had proved its worth battling against the incendiary bomb fires as well as oil and aircraft fires.

Shown a diffuser, utility and designed disarmingly simple, he said, 'Oh, we have got better gear than that.' Ken was quick. 'You think so? Let's find out. How about an exercise on Sunday?' 'Sunday?' 'Yes, I have to have the part-timers on duty at the station to be able to come here.' 'OK,' he drawled.

It was going to be a good test. Ken could see that when he arrived with his men on the Sunday. The American had an enormous oil tank, full of oil, ready for the test. 'The Yankees', as Ken quietly called them, went first. Petrol was poured over the tank and set alight.

Whoosh, smoke billowed up. 'This could be nasty, if they don't know their job,' Ken whispered to Tim Price, his No 2. Up drove the USAF firemen with their pump containing its own limited water supply, connected up their high pressure fog nozzle, complete with its armoured cabling around the hose, and soon showed they knew how to put it out. The vaunted 'fog machine' worked, but was it any better than the simple but well proven piece of British brass?

'Good show,' said Ken genuinely. 'We'll take a chance and complicate our test.' Well used to all the make-do relays that fireman across the country achieved during the bombings, Ken said he would run a water relay from a far distant static supply and then put the fire out. Eyeing it Ken thought that is going to be several thousand feet of hose

'You can't pump water that distance?' said the American. Tim chuckled, he had heard of the protestations in earlier days when Ken's studies had defied the views of 'brass hats'. 'Well, we will give it a try. Light the tank again,' said Ken.

His simple grey-painted hose layer lorry, and the heavy pump, moved right away to the water supply. As soon as the fire flared, the firemen went into action. The pump men set into the static source, and the hose layer careered at speed across the grass, flaking out just one single line of already coupled hose behind it.

Defying the rules of the instruction books – friction should stop the supply – the water kept coming up the hose. At the fire, the line was broken from the hose-layer and the solitary fireman snapped on the diffuser. Just in time, as the spray broke out he almost nonchalantly flicked it back and forth across the flames and snuffed them out. Speechless, the American could only believe it because he had seen it himself!

* * *

146

Reporter Harold was quick on the scene with his notebook when Little Miss Muffet was blazing at night. A factory in London Street, it made junkets and the fire spread rapidly. Gordon was with one of the crews battling with the flames. 'Thank God, we have the turntable ladder,' he said to his men.

They were watching the top man go right in close to the building to snatch three RAF men from upstairs windows, where they had quarters. Life was saved but there was extensive damage and food stores were destroyed.

*   *   *

Concentrating on the Fire Force Commander's concern for the historic towns, Oxford was chosen as the centre for another massive weekend exercise. Gordon Castle was put in charge of a lengthy relay from one of the static water tanks. A Home Office inspector, and a Fire Force officer with him, were watching his handling of the situation.

Then, no planned part of the work-out, one of the pumps broke down. Immediately, the 'Taplow officer', as those at Fire Force were called, started trying to tell him what to do, 'Get another pump ...' 'Leave him alone, he's in charge of it,' snapped the Home Office man.

Gordon turned to the crews, 'Cut out this pump, couple up the hose.' As soon as that was done, 'Increase the pressure,' he shouted back to the base pump. 'There's no time to get another pump. If those buildings were on fire, it would be away by the time the pump got here,' he said to the inspector.

'Good, you are quite right,' replied the man from the Home Office warmly.

The new lengths of plastic pipeline carried by lorries, with men dropping them off and clamping the joints together as it moved at a steady pace, were in use. This was another breakthrough in the efforts to beat the problems of disrupted mains.

Smoke bombs were going off all around when, in complete contrast, Henry Barnes, who was on duty as an observer, was offered an ancient college hose cart. It was the message brought with it, which was more surprising. 'Hose cart from Jesus.' Determined not to be nonplussed, Henry replied, 'I don't think it's that desperate.'

147

21 · Giving service

Rapturous applause greeted the Civil Defence personnel as they came on stage at the Palace Theatre to take the final curtain call for their remarkable Sunday show. An ambition had been realised, now that Britain was turning to the offensive from the defensive.

All the trappings were the same, steel helmets, gasmasks – ever ready – but now they could find time to do something to show their unity, and raise money for charity. Jane was especially pleased with its success, and she was to be more so when she read the newspaper's report saying, 'a dancer, both attractive and talented, who showed a definite feeling in stage-craft.'

So would her friend, Betty. Together they sang 'Alice Blue Gown', the routine that had already made them hits at the fire stations, dressed in their coloured crinolines stitched together in quiet moments. The reporter in the sparce space of those eight-page papers, said, 'Betty had a nice voice.'

But the highlight for both was encouraging and being part of the dancing team of firewomen, with their high-stepping routine. Daring it had to be, because there were no costumes to borrow. They appeared in their tunics, which just covered their navy blue pants, with black stockings and suspenders. Very appreciated but also very professional. If they had grown-up in different days they might well have gone on the stage.

Others, like Pat-le-Ron the ventriloquist, were to do so, but nobody knew for sure then.

That Sunday, the show was called 'Services Off Parade'. There was even an augmented Civil Defence orchestra, which started off with a march medley. This was to create the atmosphere for the first of two pageants, 'Britain Awakes', led by eight-year-old Dennis Anderson dressed in CD uniform.

There were a lot in the cast and the audience were delighted. People were seeing the other side of these men and women, who day and night were fighting Hitler, or giving aid to all the unavoidable casualties among our forces preparing to take the fight to Germany.

Perhaps more important at that moment was the news that the concert raised over £100 in aid of the Red Cross Penny-a-Week Fund. That was big money.

*   *   *

For this offensive airfields were constructed all over the countryside, and these kept the NFS busy. Britain's landscape was transformed, without many people realising

148

the enormity of it. 'Careless talk costs lives,' was still a slogan in people's minds – and many were so tired with their war efforts that they could hardly care.

The firemen had to care. Recognising how crashes of their own planes were affecting his men, Ken Watson decided to take some action. There wasn't much he could do when grown men retched. All he could do was to try and set an example by appearing to harden himself and take no notice.

After one particularly harrowing experience he said to Tim Price, 'We should try to arrange visits to inspect these aircraft. Let's learn what we can of the hazards – and the escape hatches, etc.'

He picked up a daily paper, pointed, and said, 'One truth we already know. People do not make rescues amid a hail of exploding bullets. The unvarnished truth is that when the heat reaches the ammo belts, the brass cartridge cases expand, the bullets become a loose fit, and when the cordite fires it pops out.'

Tim decided to join in. 'I think one of the greatest dangers is the explosion of the oxygen cylinders. When one of those quarter-inch steel beasts explodes . . . Mind you, again, others right in the centre of the heat stay safe.'

Ken nodded. 'If there is a danger from bullets, the greatest danger is from the machine guns. The moral is duck under any guns and depress them so, should they fire, the bullets go into the ground.'

British and American station commanders were grateful. Inside and out, the firemen inspected Wellingtons, Lancasters, Halifaxes, then Flying Fortresses, Liberators, and Typhoons. 'This is different from the days of the Battle of Britain,' said Ken. Tim agreed.

The firemen were taught where they could get into planes, how to depress those machine guns, in fact all they needed to know. 'Some of us can release a rear gunner from his turret in 30 seconds and, if we are blindfolded, still in under a minute,' Ken told fellow officers. He was on a NFS training course. That was not part of the training.

'What else did you learn?' was the general murmur. They, too, wanted to learn something practical. 'Watch out for the metal parts of the plane. They can become sizzling hot without showing any signs of heat. If you are careless where you put your hand, too bad!' That really had them listening.

'If a kite crashes on take-off you're dealing with over 1,000 gallons of fuel, and sometimes the tanks go up.' Almost casually, he went on, 'You get a warning when this is going to happen, well at least nine times out of ten, and if you duck and move nearer the plane, you're all right! If you move back and away, you'll invariably catch it.'

*   *   *

When the canteen van arrived brand new, it was a cheering moment. Not just because there was now a badly needed big mobile kitchen but because it came from Canada. 'They don't forget us,' said Roger Smith, 'just like the firemen who volunteered and came over.'

He was chatting to Gordon Castle as they took a breather. It did not need German

149

bombers to keep them in action during the hot summer of 1943. Drought had made the commons tinder dry. The heath fires spreading across Finchampstead Ridges, and the countryside around Ascot and Windsor, were keeping them sweating. It was the same for the firewoman driver and the cook; they collected the hot food and urn of tea from the main Reading canteen, at the last possible minute, to dash wherever needed. With all the military installations, the fires had to be controlled.

Just as important, but, a far cry from the days and nights when firewomen headed for blitzed towns with mobile canteens.

*   *   *

The challenge was thrown down by a flight lieutenant who was new to Gordon's patch. It followed a darts match at the aerodrome. Gordon was proud of his liaison with the RAF, and the men from his fire stations used to visit the sergeants' mess and enjoy a game. All had good respect for these aircrews – plucky, and they knew their job.

Gordon was back there next day making plans for a full-blown exercise when the flying officer said, 'I never rely upon your fire service much, it takes them so long to get to the aerodromes.' He was smiling as he said it but Gordon knew, somewhere in the past, there must be a reason for such a remark. Or perhaps a misgiving which ought to be cleared up.

Nobody else needed telling how proud Gordon was of his 'boys' as he called them, and their capabilities. 'Try me,' he said, 'Give them a test call.' 'What about now?' 'Any time suits me.' The RAF officer came back again, 'Should I preface the call as an exercise?' he queried. 'No, but tell my control not to pass the call on to headquarters,' replied Gordon.

The others stepped back as the two men went into the RAF's offices and, with Gordon watching, he telephoned the fire brigade. Immediately, the RAF officer looked at his watch and started timing.

Everybody knew that the aerodrome was six miles from the fire station and the road had several sharp bends, which made speeding tough for a lorry and trailer pump. Flat out they must have travelled on the straight because within ten minutes the fire bells could be heard and on to the drome swept the ATV with pump and the foam tender.

Gordon told his crews why he had summoned them and sent them straight back to the station. The flying officer's face was a picture. 'You must have tipped them off,' he spluttered. 'How could I, I was with you?' replied Gordon. All ended well, in the officers' mess over a beer. 'Your firemen certainly shook me,' he admitted, 'I take back all I said.'

Just to prove that assistance would arrive as fast as humanly possible, Gordon arranged the same thing to take place one night. With just the slits of light through the blackout shields on the headlights, the 'boys' got there in 12 minutes. Drivers used to the rigours of night travel in the blackout understood what that meant.

Gordon also felt a sense of personal pleasure when he heard that the aircraft

150

constructors at his nearest, and Reading's pre-war aerodrome, had been renamed Miles Aircraft, after its famous designer.

*   *   *

Harold Randle making his frequent mission for the firemen to the fish and chip shop, to see if they had anything to sell, was conscious of the long column of US lorries rolling by. It was a filthy wet evening. As he dodged across the road, Harold saw a jeep, going the other way, skid violently on the tram lines.

The jeep smashed into the side of one of the lorries, straight into the petrol tank. Flames leapt 50 feet into the air, instantly, high above the trolleybus cables. Harold ran into the station shouting the alarm.

Firemen scrambled to a new foam carrying fire tender, specially prepared with foam gun for fighting petrol fires. It refused to start! Just a few hundred yards along the road, an American soldier was trapped in the blazing jeep. 'Take the ATV,' shouted Roger Smith.

At the nearest hydrant they fixed a hose and, regardless of the danger without the protection of foam, Roger and a fireman walked straight into the flames, right up to the side of the jeep. They were putting their faith in pressure and the simple spray jet. It worked. The fire died as quickly as it blew up.

Harold watched with admiration. It was so quick that few would have realised the crew's bravery. Everybody's attention was on the body bag which they produced; there was no way the American soldier could have been freed, his foot was trapped under a pedal. But they had not known that.

*   *   *

It was a quiet day when Ken was asked by the officer commanding a Royal Army Service Corps unit, in a big country manse, to pay them a visit. He had taken fire precautions as laid down in the regulations, he told Ken, but he didn't think there was any danger now from air attack or incendiaries?

Wellington bombers were circling overhead from a nearby drome as they talked. 'I quite agree, but . . .' Ken paused, and nodded his head upwards. 'Oh, I think the chances of an aircraft hitting the house are very remote,' replied the officer, and that was his decision.

Three days went by then, the telephone rang. As the firewoman put the bells down, 'A Whitley bomber has crashed by the RASC manse,' she said.

It was a dreadful sight for the fire crews. Eight men aboard were killed and burnt beyond recognition. Yet it had been a miraculous escape for the house, the bomber, in trouble on exercise, had grazed the roof ridge as it swept over, then hit a tree and crumpled into a field opposite.

The soldiers and their officers were also upset by the tarpaulin sheets covering the bodies, and Ken refrained from saying, 'I told you so.'

Something Ken did not understand was still bugging him, and he decided to take his crews back there, a short while after, for an exercise. A firemen opened the

151

hydrant in the ground, as another ran out the hose. 'Water on' shouted the leading firemen, and the response dribbled out, just about 10 feet! 'It's piddling,' shouted the man on the branch.

There was no water there to fight a fire whatever fire precautions had been taken. 'The next nearest is the brook across the fields. Get to work,' ordered Ken. To reach it and run out twin lines of hose took many minutes. 'Thank God that plane didn't hit the house. They were very lucky,' he said to himself.

*   *   *

Hardly were they back at the station, than the phone rang again. It was the LPTB, operators of the London trains which ran out through the busy stations in Buckinghamshire. 'Can you help?' That same cry. Electric pumps which filled the overhead storage tanks with water had failed and main-line trains running into the station were unable to refill their boilers.

The crews were despatched at once. People relied implicitly on the trains to get to work. They were prepared to stand packed together, uncomplaining; only a blown-up track, or machine-gun-riddled engine, stopped the rail men.

Hose was laid out to a stream a quarter-of-a-mile away, and the pumping began. All night long this constant effort provided the water. Early passengers were surprised to see firemen squat on top of the header tank and patrolling the lines of hose.

The firemen were surprised too. They had not realised that these big steam trains took so many hundreds of gallons of water at a time. All through the day the work went on. As vital to the war effort were the goods trains and these were kept rolling as well. It was late the next night before the electric pumps were repaired, and the men could be dismissed.

'I wonder how many appreciate how necessary this work was,' Ken wrote in his diary. 'Any delay would have hindered the war material.'

*   *   *

It was a cryptic message from the NFS hierarchy which led to another strange special service call. 'Send a mobile dam and crew to Surrey and keep in convoy with a lorry proceeding from there into Buckinghamshire carrying a load of phosphorous bombs.'

Riding 'shotgun' to high-risk convoys of ammunition vehicles was normal. They would take them to the boundary and pass on to other firemen. Firemen were puzzled when they found themselves regularly required to escort convoys of very long, large crates. Later, they understood, when they stood by as the airborne troops took off in their uncrated gliders.

Phosphorous, though, was not the fireman's best friend. Early one morning the Police called to warn that they had found the deadly chemical on a road! Ken set off with a crew. Globules were glistening in the moonlight. They were right across the road and stretched for about 15 feet.

152

Damp from morning dew was already making it hard to trace. Ken and his men were soon on their hands and knees, casting the moon's shadows before them. Every time they saw the glow of phosphorous they carefully picked it up on the point of a penknife and transferred it to a jar of water.

'We must have looked barmy, but nobody saw us,' he told Tim when they got back. 'But we couldn't ignore it, anybody could have picked it up on their boots and taken it somewhere else, or on a tyre it could have burned and started a fire.

*   *   *

At one of the USAAF aerodromes an American lieutenant and Ken were discussing water supply problems. Crash tenders on their dromes carried their own water supply, very similar to the fire brigade's mobile dams, but mix the foam compound in the pump itself. When empty they had to be provided with more water.

The American's headache was that his large trailer pump could not meet their needs. 'How can we keep them filled?' he asked Ken. Outside the dromes the NFS regularly kept the tenders topped up, but this was different. 'Let us run an exercise and sort it out?' It was agreed.

Deciding on the furthest fire risk from the mains, Ken said, 'We can put a sportapool dam there, fill it with water, and then your crash tenders and our pump can work from it. It will supply all our needs.'

A Sunday morning was chosen for the exercise, which brought the part-time men into it as well. It seemed no time at all before the pumps were pouring water through the hose and filling the dam.

The American, new to England, watched amazed. 'Theoretically, No,' he said. 'At technical school I was told it was impossible to relay water all that way without using far more pumps than you were. I'm getting more water than I could possibly use!' 'Our book experts tell us the same thing here,' grunted Ken.

For the firemen it was also different. Strange to have to keep their eyes on the runway as they patrolled their lines, or moved any vehicle. They were avoiding Flying Fortresses and Liberators which seemed only feet above their heads, becoming airborne just before reaching where the line was laid!

But life was not all one-upmanship. Ken liked their attitude, and dislike of red tape! For months afterwards he was risking the wrath of his seniors as he retold the story of the Flying Fortress which crashed on another aerodrome, neighbouring the Americans.

'As they heard it come down,' recounted Ken, 'they turned out with all their equipment, breakdown crane, the lot, and were on the job within 15 minutes. They didn't waste time obtaining permission to go, or waiting for the call – they just acted. How surprised they must be with all our red-tape.'

Maybe that was why Ken was still waiting to learn the result of his promotion training course. It was strange, results always came through quickly and the grapevine hints – very frightened and veiled – were that he had done well, perhaps even come top!

*　　*　　*

Fog was another hazard for firemen, driving with virtually no headlights. All knew it was lousy outside but it made no difference when the bells clattered. As the doors swung open, there was nothing to be seen. Jack was driving and he shouted to Roger Smith to look for the nearside kerb as he set off across the road and turned right.

'It's the bakery at the bottom of Beecham Road, going well,' said Roger. 'At least it's not far,' said Jack. But, even crossing the road seemed a long way. They found the kerb and set off. 'I've lost it,' suddenly shouted Roger. 'Here it comes,' tersely responded Jack, swinging his wheel as he realised he had crossed the main road. 'Thank God nothing is about.'

The bakehouse behind the shop was ablaze and Harold Randle made his way inside to the roof, while others climbed the ladder outside. He realised, with surprise, that just those feet into the air lifted him into much thinner fog. 'Jerry can see better than we can,' he said, quite shocked. 'I hope he's not around to see this,' said Roger.

The heat from the overworked ovens – Reading's population had grown immensely to handle all the war work – had ignited wood set in the bricks. Already burning through the roof, it was a roman candle. Precarious work, as Harold was helping the crew the flooring gave way beneath him. He fell directly on to the hot ovens. Not nice, he was quickly helped to safety.

His uniform was damaged – after all this time it had still looked smart, despite regularly sleeping in it – and he was given a navy blue battledress, without coupons.

22 · Colour scheme

They came in their hundreds, with all their equipment. The NFS men and women who reinforced Southern England, for the Harlequin exercise, were further backed up by more from regions in the North and North West. It was an incredible domestic invasion. Cover for those parts of the country was denuded as preparations were made to combat the expected heavy retaliatory bombing when the Invasion of Europe was launched.

Ken wrote in his diary, 'I hear there are more than 11,000 men and women coming, and they are bringing 1,200 fully equipped pumps, towing vehicles, ready for anything.' Coaches and trains brought the others. The code name was 'Colour Scheme'.

Reinforcing stations in Fire Force 15 were set up. The major ones were at Harpsden Court, near Henley; Heath End House, south of Aldermaston; Upton Court, near Didcot; and Bray Court. Chantry House, close to Bray Church, became a hostel for firewomen – they were all in it. Everywhere local firemen were finding other 'homes' for new crew-mates.

It was hard work for everyone while the frantic preparations went ahead. 'Places have to be prepared for these men, and for their pumps,' Ken explained to his station crews. 'Large country houses are being commandeered and all of us have to get stuck in fitting them out. At least they will receive a different reception to some of our blitz calls!

'It means scrubbing and cleaning out, and fitting in bunks and bedding, and rest rooms. Everything, even writing tables and pens and nibs. We are housing large groups at a time, so, in some cases, the building squads will be going in first, taking out fire-places and putting in cooking ranges to cope with the task.

'Let's do what we can to make them as comfortable as possible. They are not here just for the invasion and any trouble that may bring, but to help us with local fire cover.'

Everybody kept asking questions; the war was really taking a new and exciting twist. 'Will we have to follow the troops and go to Europe?' asked Tim, quietly afterwards. 'I don't know, but it makes sense,' said Ken.

*   *   *

On the day the Colour Scheme men were due to arrive, Ken was at a big house ensuring everything was ready for them. He was with the reinforcing company officer and his section leader. It was not to be a peaceful day. A telephone message came from the fire station that its crew was called out.

The relief control room girl was a stranger to the district. All she could tell Ken, in answer to his questions was that the crew had turned right outside the station and the fire was outside the town.

All three jumped into Ken's staff car and dashed back to the station. There they could see, way ahead, a mass of smoke spreading across the sky. Clearly there was trouble. Shouting to the girl to notify divisional control, he jumped into the driver's seat of another of the tenders and pumps lined up, and off they raced as fast as they could go.

Into view as they turned the last corner was a large country house, ablaze from top to bottom. Tim and his crew were hard at work. There was half a gale blowing to fan the flames. Flying embers, smoke and the intense heat were real dangers, and Ken could see the first crew were pretty nearly all in.

A large pond in the grounds was providing the water for the first pump. Ken, and the other two officers, pulled their pump over the lawn and down the slope to it. 'There's not enough water to keep both pumps going,' grunted Ken in disgust. Both the others agreed. 'There's a stream about a quarter-of-mile away,' said a gardener. 'We shall have to run a relay. Where's the despatch rider?'

He had heard Ken's shout and appeared like magic. 'Take a message back. Make pumps four.' Three men helped Ken and the section leader haul the pump back to the tender and hitch on. 'It's up to us to go and find the stream,' said Ken to the visiting section leader. 'None of those men can be spared.'

Eventually they found the stream. Unhitching the pump, the section leader was left to jack it up and get the suction off and coupled up on his own, Ken ran out 1,000 feet of hose on his own. He did it by unrolling 100 feet of hose, then driving the ATV forward the same distance and running out another 100 feet. Ten times he repeated it.

Just as it was done a reinforcing pump arrived, coupled up to his hose line and set off laying out their own towards the fire. The section leader was just as practical as Ken, he started the pump and began running the water through to save precious time. He did not wait for the training school and rulebook signals

The driver's seat of Ken's ATV was smouldering, ignited by a burning ember. He felt dead beat, his shirt was sticking to him, sodden with perspiration.

Just then a senior officer arrived to take charge. 'Go back to your station, the Colour Scheme men have arrived and are waiting to go to the house.' Ken settled the Northerners in and arranged their feeding, and organised relief crews for the men at the fire.

Next morning he was summoned to headquarters and severely slated for not being in a properly dressed condition to report to a superior officer on his arrival at the fire ground. 'I found you running out hose like an ordinary fireman, with your jacket off and in your shirt sleeves...'

'What depths has this service sunk to?' Ken asked Tim as he privately recounted the rebuke. 'I have heard of this happening elsewhere but I found it rather hard to believe. The days when an officer worked with his men, and showed them he knew his job, seem to be fast disappearing.

'Under nationalisation, apparently officers must strut about like a popinjay. Jealousy is rife enough, but it looks as though you have to be a Yes man to succeed. Perhaps we ought to indent for kid gloves!'

Meanwhile as the contingents arrived in 15 Fire Force, those in Ken's own station, were soon in the hot seat. They had just finished their welcoming dinner when the bells went down. That fire-fighting job kept them up half the night.

Sure enough, the call came, 'Volunteers are needed for an Overseas Contingent'. Men from the colour scheme reinforcements were ready to volunteer just as Ken and his men were too. Most passed the medical with no trouble at all. 'Why the hell has no reason been given?' asked an angry Ken, as he, like a lot of the others, were bluntly turned down.

* * *

One never knew what to expect when sent to a strange station on duty. Betty arrived at U-station during the Colour Scheme reinforcements from the North of England. As she walked into the control room, there was a sigh of relief. 'We haven't a cook, today,' said Roger Smith. Instead of handling the control room, Betty was busy cooking for 40.

* * *

The rebuke given to Ken by a senior officer continued to rankle – dressed down for not being in 'proper uniform, full fire-fighting kit, and ready to report to him' when he arrived at a fire. It was obvious to Tim, who alone knew, but Ken was far too busy to realise how much it had upset him. After all, but for the speed with which Ken and the stranger, a section leader, had achieved the water relay, the country house would have been gutted.

But Ken, at the back of his mind, kept remembering the previous incident. He knew of officers who seemed to have been moved to different zones, because they did not see eye to eye with superior officers. And, how, until he was in trouble, he had never believed the stories of anonymous letters written about officers, which were acted upon. He was always too much involved in his real world of fighting the war to recognise the tribulations of setting up one national fire service at great speed. Rough justice, and sometimes bad judgment, were bound to happen in choosing officers.

Observation posts were being set up across the country by the NFS so that, when there was enemy raiding, fires could be seen and pinpointed and the information passed immediately to headquarters. It was an important move in countryside so transformed with aerodromes and military bases.

A huge factory was chosen. 'No sir, a good view, but, if it's hit it will be too dangerous for the men stuck up there,' said Ken.

His choice was a large church in the centre of the town's square. 'If the church is

157

hit, the look-out at the top will still be trapped,' Ken pointed out, 'but he can have a rope to get down.' He thought, 'There is a problem. It is not a straightforward drop. How do we know how long a rope he will need?'

That started a discussion at the station without resolve, until Ken said, 'I will try it myself. I will do it after Saturday evening's exercise.' To the part-timers' section leader, he said, 'I want you to come with me. We are going to the highest point in the church, tie a 100 feet line, and I am coming down the outside as far as that will reach and then continue in stages.'

Two new firewomen had recently joined. 'Bring them along to the exercise, to see the start, the how and why, of messages they handle.'

Ken briefed his men carefully for the 'escape by rope' from the tower top. He took a normal coil and arranged for firemen to be at key points. Tieing the rope carefully on the very top of the high tower, Ken stopped long enough to enjoy the disarmingly peaceful view. 'Why the hell are we doing all these things,' he thought. Then over the side he went, down past the clock face, to the end of the rope and sought a vantage point.

'Untie the rope,' shouted up Ken, as he clung precariously. The coil, although dropped carefully almost unseated him. He was playing a dangerous game and he quickly slipped the end to a second fireman.

This time the rope was tied to a gargoyle. It was going to be easy, the next drop led to a flat roof – 'We will need 185 feet of rope,' he thought. As he tried to move, Ken realised the gargoyle was also moving! He hung on to the building. The section leader realised his dilemma. 'Sir, there is nothing else I can tie it to!'

Ken realised that he could not move. Softly, he said, 'Don't broadcast it but I am trapped. Nip down and tell Tim to bring a ladder.'

The doors of the fire station were thrust open, out drove the pump escape with its bell ringing furiously. Straight to the church it drove. Off came the ladder, and it was raised up the side of the church. 'I'll kill you buggers,' shouted Ken. Tim came smartly up the ladder, 'Shall I carry you down, sir?'

Hot and thirsty after such exercise on a sultry evening, Ken invited the two firewomen to join him for a drink in the pub across the square. Control knew where to find him.

Several days later, Ken was ordered to headquarters. Waving an anonymous letter, the officer said, 'You, an officer, took two firewomen into a public house.' He was called to account to justify his actions.

Repeating the interview to Tim, Ken said, 'Other officers have experienced the same thing. One told me he found it rather hard not to distrust everyone he met in the course of duty.

'Personally, if my actions and orders are causing enemies then I am sure they must be right and proper. At least I am getting things done.'

Tim was obviously busting to say something else. 'Have you heard the latest absurdity? I have just had a call from Jim, an inspector has been to his station and played hell about all the equipment carried on his ATVs.

'He would not accept that in the country a crew needs extra gear to reach many fires. And to cope with haystack fires and the like.'

Ken groaned. 'I know,' he said, 'nationalisation has laid down that only a set amount of hose shall be carried.' 'Yes, and he played hell because there was more than the one diffuser nozzle to spray hay and heath fires.'

'They were ordered to take off all the hose, nozzles and the hay knives and forks because they were not standard equipment. That would mean most times a crew would have to call for reinforcements simply to reach a water supply.'

Another sigh from Ken, 'Why don't the divisional officers make their voices heard, they know this equipment is necessary? What did Jim do?'

Tim laughed. 'As soon as the inspectorate left the station, he put it all back on!'

It was not long before Ken had a visitation and was ordered to take off his extra hose. 'I have just saved a cottage by running 1,500 feet of hose and using one pump. Do you want me to send three pumps every time that happens in the country?' 'Take it off,' said the officer. Ken did – and put it back on.

*   *   *

The RAF officer appeared to know his job, he oozed efficiency. Walking into Aylesbury's fire station, he made it clear in a few words that he was not intending to give much away. 'I understand I can count on full liaison between our services?' He did not wait for a reply. 'I don't know much about fire fighting, will you come and give me some advice?'

Ken Watson said, 'Of course.' Off they went. There were armed sentries on the gate as they arrived. He followed the officer into the main building, and the first thing he saw was all the girls working down one side, wearing a special tammy hat. It was the fact that they were ATS, Wrens, and Waafs, all working as one, which caught his attention.

Then he realised that the men were all mixed too, Army, Navy and RAF, plus civilians. Ken was given some old fashioned looks, they were clearly eyeing him up and down and not liking what they saw. But with the senior RAF officer leading the way nothing was said.

Ken toured the building, climbed on to the roof, satisfied himself that all was well and gave his advice to the officer. 'Thank you,' said the officer, who personally saw Ken off the premises.

Talking quietly to Tim Price – he believed that his number 2 should always be well briefed in case he should be another killed in action – Ken said, 'I think we have something important to keep an eye on at Bletchley. You could see they were all professionals, and they did not like me around.'

It was not long before a senior fire officer was on the telephone. 'Have you been contacted by an RAF officer?' 'Yes sir.' 'You didn't tell me?' Ken's mind alerted. 'There was no need, sir. He asked for advice on fire fighting and I gave it under our instructions to give aid to the Services.'

Bletchley had not been mentioned by name and Ken realised that it was being avoided over an ordinary telephone line. 'Well, you will forget that such a place exists and you will forget that you have been there!' 'Right sir, if that is what you say, I will forget it.'

There was no question of Ken ever doing anything to put the war effort in jeopardy – 'Walls have ears' and all the other placarded posters were everywhere. But he was curious and it did not take long to find a reason to go to his headquarters. 'What was wrong?' he asked the officer when they were in private. 'It's not for me to discuss it but you must completely forget that you ever went near the place. And, the officer has been shifted!'

Ken did forget it, there were too many other matters to worry about. It was raining hard, a filthy evening, some time later, when Ken, returning from Bicester, saw two Service girls walking. Both were wearing the tammys. Pulling up, 'Would you like a lift?' Subconsciously, he realised how hard they stared at him, and then at the insignia on the car door, before getting into the rear.

There was dead silence, and to make conversation Ken said, casually, 'Where you off to, Bletchley?' Both stiffened. 'Will you stop the car, please.' They opened the door and got out without another word.

Sometime later, headquarters sent for Ken. 'Here are instructions which are secret and confidential to be opened in the event of a call to Bletchley Park.' The envelope was passed over and the officer added, 'In the event of a call there, the crews are to stop outside the main drive and to await further instructions. The sentries will tell them when the guard dogs have been rounded up. It will not be safe for any of them to enter the drive alone. They could be shot or got by the dogs.'

Not until the last days of the war did Ken learn that it was the listening station intercepting and decoding the Nazis' radio transmissions, and receiving coded messages sent back by saboteurs, and other secret agents, operating in the occupied countries.

At the time he gave the girls a lift, he was thinking more of the words of the Pathfinders' pilot whom he had picked up the previous night. He wanted to go to High Wycombe, and the Toc H. 'Come to the station, we'll put you up for the night,' said Ken.

The pilot told him, as they drove, how they put down flares over Hamburg and then the 'blockbuster' bombs had blown them out. 'We had to go in again.' Arriving at the fire station, he looked at the long extendable ladder, with its huge wheels, on the pump escape. 'I couldn't go up there, I'd pass out with fright!'

*   *   *

One of the first aboard a new breed of light wooden landing craft was Harold Randle. He was proud to go, and was quick to tell Roger Smith when he reported on duty. They were being built in Reading in great secrecy. No word slipped out, now it was time to boost morale by telling the local people.

Harold, the reporter, was invited to take a trip – on the Thames not the sea. Simple, a long flat-bottomed craft, with small ramp which lowered at the front. 'It oozes all the loving care that the craftsmen of Elliotts' joinery firm can put into the time they have. I wonder where it will fight?'

'Wood?' said Roger. 'Apparently, it's less likely to sink if it is hit badly,' said

160

Harold. 'The only metal protection is a tiny square 'chimney' where the man at the helm will stand up above everybody else. I wouldn't want that job.'

The infantry landing craft slipped up river as far as Mapledurham, turned and returned. No champagne across the bows, just another surprise from Reading's war effort.

*   *   *

A column of tanks, something like 50, came rumbling along the road. Approaching Gordon like a lethal, ghostly centipede, he swung his car off the road on to the grass verge for safety. It was a dark, wet night, and he was on his way back from visiting one of his part-timers' stations. The days always had to be stretched, because the night hours were the only time the men could leave their work and switch to being fire-fighters.

Huge tanks like these practically filled the road; they roared on with hardly a light on at all. All Gordon had showing were the official regulation, and very dim, sidelights. But as they ground past, some of the drivers shouted 'Turn them off, you're blinding us!'

'How the hell do they do it?' asked Gordon, as he warned his crews of yet another major danger when hurrying to a fire. 'Some of those drivers seem to have a sixth-sense – or some other secret weapon.' 'Like infra-red?' quipped a leading fireman. 'Well, at least they stand a good chance, if they're that efficient,' noted Gordon. 'It will give the Nazi Panzers some of their own medicine.'

*   *   *

As NFS efficiency grew, a massive pump was installed on the bank of the Thames, near Tilehurst station. A pipeline ran up the embankment and under the main railway lines, to a massive dam on the main road. It was to provide 2,000 gallons a minute, a brilliant, if expensive, move to provide cover for the west side of town. A tough task which drew the attention of senior officers.

To be prepared, the officer responsible for its placement checked the day before their official visit. He made sure there was plenty of depth of water where the pump would suck thirstily. Early next morning he met the divisional officer and the 'authority' and took them to the Thames.

Disaster! When they arrived, the river was drained very low. The scene was quite exceptional with the chalk banks showing – and the concrete sump for the pump was three inches above water! There was no way it would collect water. Because the Thames Conservancy had a problem, their men were holding the river back at Whitchurch weir and had let it all out at Caversham.

Another day, another visit, it worked perfectly. But the war was nearly over. No one could guess then that, within months, the pump, thank God, would never be used in anger. But as the Invasion troops freed Holland, the pump was quickly recovered and taken to Holland, to help the Dutch people in pumping out their land flooded by the breached dykes. Firemen also were to hurry to the coast with loads of piping needed for the pipelines – to pump away water. It was a strange contrast.

23 · Invasion – D Day

Whenever the station bells ring, the adrenalin always begins to pump. It did when the call came from the aerodrome. Figures hurtled towards the appliance room; in that split second the lights were on the indicator board: ATV and FT. The firewoman knew what was needed, the pump and foam tender. 'Where's the job, miss?' asked Ken Watson as he bundled into her control room. 'Aerodrome! Wants all available help.'

'Must be something big for that message,' thought Ken. 'Send the MDU, the mobile dam unit, as well.' The big trailer pump was already going out through the door – a slick turnout. 'Where is my despatch rider?' Looking round as he ran to his car, he realised he was already outside, revving the bike's engine, waiting for his boss.

Down the road they raced. The ATV was speeding, safely but not wasting a second. The foam tender was behind him and, just in his mirror, was the MDU, striving vainly to keep with them as the driver fought to handle his load of water.

The despatch rider ahead of Ken was trying to clear the road. Ken accelerated around the ATV, the driver grinned and gave him a gesticulation. A toot from Ken and the DR dropped in behind him and ahead of the ATV, to give it the best chance. Stopping a lorry suddenly, with a heavy trailer pushing up your backside, isn't funny.

Ken saw the pillar of smoke ahead. 'Looks like petrol,' he thought. 'Wonder what's happened?' He looked at the speedo, '64 from a Morris 10!'

Sharp left-hand bend, the car skidded round that one. 'Phew!' but Ken kept going, still two miles to go – and nearly all bends. He just caught a glimpse of the ATV in his mirror – 'Blimey, they are shifting. Must have seen the smoke.'

It was getting much worse. 'Good Lord, it's near the hangars.' The entrance guards were frantically waving him on. As he passed the RAF's own fire station he could see it was empty, all the appliances were out. 'So it is something big.' All this talking to himself was really just going through his thoughts as he prepared his mind for action.

'Shall I go back for the MDU?' shouted the despatch rider as he pulled up. 'No, he knows this place inside out,' said Ken. 'Leave your bike, stick with me.'

A hangar was on fire, planes inside were blazing. 'Christ, what a mess.' He caught his breath, he could smell bodies.

Running across the grass, Ken shouted to a sergeant. 'What's up? My boys are on their way.'

'Two Wellington bombers, Typhoon fighter, and Queen Mary low loader. The hanger doors crashed down trapping some WAAFs and bomber crew,' he replied. 'No hope for them is there?' said Ken, and he shook his head. 'All right sergeant, here's the boys, we'll get to work at the hydrant at the rear and work up towards you. Can we have a few RAF chaps to help carry the foam to the inductor?'

He rattled out crisp, clear orders. As soon as the pump pressure began to build, Ken turned back to his own crew. 'We will get inside. And we can also cover up those bodies with foam, stop people gaping.' He added, half aloud, 'I wonder if those blasted oxygen cylinders will behave!'

Pointing, he said, 'Drive your foam on to that metal, that's right, it will bounce into the flames at the back of the engine. We can't reach it from here with that dammed hangar door jammed.'

He swore. 'I haven't sent the Stop message, the old man will be tearing his hair out.'

The despatch rider had been with his officer long enough to admire his qualities, and he wasn't likely to repeat any such 'disrespectful' conversation. Ken Watson wasn't a yes-man. The despatch rider had seen the fingered salute of the laughing pump driver, but he knew it was loyal camaraderie typical of the men who would go to extremes for their boss, like risking their necks in that hangar.

'Sticky job,' Ken said as his Column Officer superior arrived. We have nearly got it under control. A Wellington was taking off, an engine failed, the undercarriage collapsed, and the plane skidded over here. It transfixed another Wellington, struck that four-ton lorry, set it on fire, then hit the hangar door, bringing it down across the Queen Mary.

'The WAAFs were loading another Wellington on to the low-loader and it trapped them and the crew under it. Then the heat fired that Typhoon and damaged the side of the hangar.'

A good summary, but rather an understatement of what had been going on. But then war-time fire fighting was often like that.

*   *   *

'Hitler's Luftwaffe has turned on the pressure,' wrote Ken. 'London, January 21, 1944.' Interference with the enemy's VHF radio navigation beams, and radar warning as they took off, enabled the NFS top officers to be alert to a new offensive as it started. Attacks were short and sharp, and they were also widespread, as renewed efforts were made to disrupt sleep, and so the war effort.

Firemen in London were to face Heinkels dropping two 2,500kg bombs. The new huge incendiary containers were unloading 620 heavier fire bombs, many now explosive or, like the butterfly, booby traps.

From the noise, and the purple and red warnings, there were hundreds of sorties. 'They must be making double trips again,' was John Lander's view, as he stood in the road and looked east.

The second on the 29th found the NFS busy across a wide area of Southern England. Tom Goldsmid was quick to tell John Lander 'The East End has been hit. A railway station has been copped, killing quite a few. I think it's Leytonstone.'

February saw more bad fires in London, and across the countryside. 'But the bombers are avoiding the heaviest defences,' said John. 'They must be creeping round the coast and then coming in.'

Tom was back again in the middle of February. 'Nasty night for fires in London. All over in 30 minutes.' John had to change his mind a few days later when Reading was the target zone.

So it continued, at night, a new Baby Blitz. Again, after a respite, as March began. London was still the main target but at the end of the month, bombs were scattered across Fire Force 15. The locals were in action, so were others across the southern counties, as a big force of bombers swept in on two nights. They came as far as Oxford and Reading.

Quiet again. 'He has lost a lot of planes,' said Roger to Harold, as they chatted, standing by. London and its suburbs took it again, with a major attack during the night of April 18. Forty or more died. But for them it seemed to be the end.

Bristol was still in Hitler's mind and the planes tried repeatedly, without success, to hit the port as the American troops and their weapons came ashore in an endless stream for the forthcoming invasion.

Sirens continued, but his bombers could not keep it up. When it sounded finally, in June, nobody could celebrate because they did not know. And, a new terror weapon was already in the skies.

*   *   *

'The Duchess of Kent is coming to visit us.' The excited news spread rapidly around the divisional staff at the Prospect Park mansion. It was a real morale booster. Not only for the way they had put the organisation together, but also 'improved' the building. That was still pretty basic, but there was some lino on the floor now.

At least their efforts were being recognised. Excitement grew as the staff paraded, especially among the girls. Two were despatched to the park gates to meet Her Royal Highness. They never made it. Suddenly everyone realised that two other girls were approaching with a lady out of uniform. It must be the Duchess! Everyone flushed up. Pam called, 'Attention' – just in time.

*   *   *

Readiness by the Americans to take action without worrying about red tape was admired by Ken. But he was left speechless when he was ordered to go to Brill fire station, in Buckinghamshire. The US soldiers did not have long to prepare themselves for the invasion and they exercised with great realism.

As he neared there were visible signs of the soldiers' preparations. Trenches were dug in people's front gardens and machine guns set in position. Tanks had cut swathes through the woods; there was a trail of trees knocked down.

Whether 'locals' liked it or not, it was happening. At least they knew the Americans paid for the damage.

Ken had been sent because of this message, 'A tank going along the road, in front of the station, saw an "enemy" tank so he turned round and burst straight through the fire station doors. He knocked them for six.'

Up came an American officer as soon as he saw Ken arrive. 'How much do we owe you?' 'I can't do that,' said Ken. I will have to report back to HQ and they will send someone to assess the damage.'

'Oh, hell,' was the reply. 'We shall be on the invasion front by then. Let me pay you now. How much do you want?' 'Sorry, I can't do it,' insisted Ken.

'You Limeys, and your red tape ... ' He was blowing his top as he marched off. 'Good luck in the fighting,' shouted Ken, after him.

Shortly after Wolverton fire station was also in trouble. A crashing Wellington bomber 'threw' one of its engines into the garden of the firemen's section leader, and the crash blast blew the station's doors wide open and off their hinges. Who would pay for that was going to take a lot longer to sort out. It was a British plane!

*   *   *

Most of Ken's diary now seemed to be not about Germans but the Services' casualties as they took the attack back. This time, however, he wrote about the NFS: 'Five hundred men and women, full and part-time took part in the second anniversary parade at Aylesbury. A message from the Home Secretary, Mr Herbert Morrison, was read telling the fire-fighters, 'You have been outstanding ...'

*   *   *

Frantic efforts were being made to prepare for the invasion, D-Day. Special courses were set up. 'Why such a panic?' asked Tim Price when he learned that Ken Watson was off on another. This time it was to absorb, 'very quickly' the finer points of rescue work. 'Shades of the People's Pantry,' had been Ken's first thought. 'If Jerry hits back at the ports and any of our big towns on the main coast roads, it's likely to be with high explosive bombs, not incendiaries,' answered Ken.

'But, if he plasters places with HE the Rescue Service is going to be taxed to the limit. It's undermanned as you know. There are not likely to be many big fires so we will be able to co-operate with the Rescue.'

Tim nodded, 'Much of their equipment is already carried on our NFS tenders, ladders, crowbars, shovels, first-aid kit, ropes, lamps ...' 'All right, I know,' responded Ken, his mind already turning over what could be achieved. 'The important thing is if a fire does break out on a rescue, we shall have pumps right on the spot.'

The course, for about 20 specially chosen fire officers, took place at the Rescue Parties Training School, near Basingstoke, and was packed into two weeks. Ken flicked the pages of the syllabus given in advance and showed long-suffering wife, Lucy. When he was not away, or on duty, he was still trying to help his father with the hairdressing business. A contrast in tasks!

Back at the station, he said to Tim, 'Listen to this. Use of derricks and lifting tackle, first-aid, tunnelling, shoring of buildings, weights and strengths of different materials.' He paused, 'Now, in February, in this bitter cold and snow. Thank goodness the building department has promised leather boots.'

Ken's apprehension soon disappeared. It was a good course and absolutely different to anything experienced in the NFS. In the grounds of the training school, a replica of part of a blitzed town had been reproduced, with streets and heaps of rubble where 'houses' once stood. This was where Ken and the others put into practice the theory learned in the lectures and from Ministry of Information and Rescue films.

A special 'incident', in freezing weather, completed the course. Several 'casualties' were laying about in the street and 'houses'. Some were trapped under debris. One Rescue man remained buried under debris for nearly an hour before being located. He was stiff with cold – but still quite cheerful! 'That's dedication,' said Ken to his neighbour.

The instructor in first-aid drew Ken's admiration. 'He was the clearest, concise, and practical lecturer, I have heard,' he told Tim. 'We all came away with a feeling of competence that we certainly did not possess before.' 'Gosh, and I always thought you were pretty hot at first-aid,' responded Tim.

Embarrassed, Ken pressed on. 'Now we have finished the course, the authorities have suddenly realised the formidable task for 20 officers is to teach 15,000 full and part-time firemen rescue training. And, it has to be completed in three or four weeks!'

'That's impossible,' exclaimed Tim. 'I hope not,' said Ken. 'It's clear with all the mobilising exercises that the invasion cannot be far away.

'Local authorities are being asked to help. The Rescue service is sending its van and equipment round the stations to explain its uses, and give lectures wherever possible.'

A few days later Tim found Ken exploding. A lecturer had sent in a bill. 'Here we have two services striving to co-operate, and some clown wants to be paid for it!

'Just think we all gave up 18 months to train before the war, and all our part-time men still get nothing for the hellish risks they take, and he cannot spare three hours!'

It was the only incident and Ken set about it with enthusiasm. He could see its value when the balloon went up. So, too, could the others in Fifteen Fire Force

Another officer gave Ken the inspiration he needed. He knew a large house which had been used by the Army for commando training. Now it was in the hands of the Home Guard. It was just what Ken wanted: very little of the roof was left, there were no windows, most floor boards missing, and it had ominous gaps in the walls.

Two hours at a time, firemen worked their way through the training. They learnt to locate casualties, bandage them, strap them on stretchers, and lower to safety through the joists, or out through the window holes. Some men even wangled it so that they could attend twice. Ken smiled, that was unusual, but he said nothing.

Firemen were trained in record time. 'We are as ready as we can be,' declared Ken. Still the waiting went on. Large scale exercises continued, usually ending at a reinforcement base, clearly spots picked carefully. Much care seemed to be going into picking these bases, in the careful parking of the lines of tenders and pumps, and the feeding and sleeping accommodation for the firemen.

All leave was cancelled. The road leading into Prospect Park, to Reading's divisional headquarters in the mansion, came alive again. Often it had been used by NFS convoys heading for blitzed towns, especially from London, as a resting spot. But now, under the protection of the huge avenues of oaks, there were solid phalanxes of fire engines. They were all part of the Colour-Scheme extra protection plan, from the north of England. Many other places were 'alive' as marshalling spots.

Harold, and the other messengers who manned the field telephone van, worked long and hard to set up field telephone communications around the park. It was a tall order feeding out the drums of cable and hanging the wires from the branches, high enough to escape the ladders. After all their practice in more urban situations, now it was so different and full of problems.

He reported to the communications officer. 'We cannot make clear lines. That last drum of cable has shorts all over the place. We've tried with the pins to eliminate the bad patch but it won't do. We shall have to use different cable.' The officer was under pressure, he knew the lads were doing their best at a critical time. But he smiled, especially as he remembered how they had all found pairs of darts, chopped off the tops and soldered on wires to make testers. At least they were using them for real.

The problem was put right after a struggle. It was just in time to be used for the invasion exercise in the town. And for the field telephone van, with Leading Fireman 'Sibby' Beeson driving the team, to be ready to take part.

Small scale versions of the reinforcement exercise were going on frequently, day and night, in divisions and areas. A special check was made to ensure all equipment of incoming crews was correct. It gave the men a training in what was expected of them – everybody thought the days ahead were going to be bloody in the south.

Either five pumps, with a section leader in charge, or ten pumps, with a company officer, two section leaders, and complete with two despatch riders, were regularly called. Meticulous records were kept of the time taken to collect the crews and pumps together, the time they left their home town, and when they arrived at the reception base. 'It's very different from those early days, when the AFS were charging off on their own to London and the like,' Sibby Beeson reminded Harold. 'Especially when you see curls sticking out from underneath despatch riders' crash helmets. All the girls are doing a great job.'

*   *   *

Ken had promised to attend a town council meeting and he was there when he received another of these 'shouts' for an Invasion Exercise. 'Sorry,' he said, leaving and dashing back to the station. He piled his kit into his staff car and, within ten minutes was on the road striving to catch up with his ten pumps. He knew their route – everything was pre-determined – and caught up with his company near to Odiham.

On the journey to the coast reinforcing base, he noticed large numbers of troops, tanks, lorries, and other equipment stationed in fields, and under trees. They seemed everywhere, in woods and ditches, with black faces. 'More than usual about. I have never seen an exercise like this,' he said to himself, but thought no more of it.

His company spent a quiet night at the Hampshire reception base, disturbed only by the large number of aircraft flying. In the morning all noticed how many aircraft there were over the coast, 'Have you ever seen so many aircraft?' Ken asked casually – and they left for home.

Calling into Reading as a stop, to give the men a breather, he met his old friend John Lander. 'What was it like, guv'nor?' 'What?' 'The invasion,' replied John. They did not know until they got back to Reading that the Invasion of Europe had started during the night!

*   *   *

John and others had been fighting huge heath fires which had been given priority for a fortnight. Enormous numbers of men and equipment had been involved. Suddenly these were forgotten. Soon after midnight, the order came, 'Pack up, back to your stations'. It was D-Day.

It was not over, there was a long, long road to go. To fireman who had fought regularly from 1940, it was good to see so many others now had the chance to fight back. Soon such fires became major tasks again. And the V1s came – and then the V2s, the rockets.

*   *   *

The tiny planes with the strange bubble and flare from the tail, and the almost two-stroke noise of its engine, had people looking at the sky again. Suddenly, silence. Without more propulsion, the plane dived. If you were lucky it disappeared out of sight, then an explosion. The V1 had arrived.

This pilotless plane, loaded with high explosives, gave a new twist to Civil Defence. It was the topic of conversation as people described their first sight of this new terror. 'One thing seems clear,' said Roger Smith to Harold, 'If it's overhead when the engine cuts, you are safe. If it is coming towards you, and has not reached you, start praying.'

Hundreds of them were arriving, scattered across a wide area, although mostly aimed for London. Clearly 'aimed' was a very general term. Harold and his girl friend were enjoying a peaceful evening in their punt on the Thames, when in the distance across the sky sped a 'doodle-bug'. Silence, bang. It was instinct to hurry back to the station. But clearly times were different.

One bomb hole, rarely was there much fire, and the nearest station could handle that. No more dashing off to provide reinforcement. This one had landed at Earley

168

and Harold, and others who still jumped to action, were not needed. Twelve landed in Berkshire, the surrounding counties also had unwelcome attention.

Tom Goldsmid took news into John Lander's office in August. 'A doodle-bug has hit a Chigwell fire station. It sounds very nasty.' But that was all he knew. By September, he realised that even his news sources could not explain the stories of the sudden massive explosions without any warning! 'Was this the rocket attacks that Churchill had hinted at in the summer?' was all he could surmise.

*   *   *

Soon huge heath fires became major tasks again. The V1s kept coming – and now it was the V2s, the rockets.

No warning, just a violent devastation of a large area, with the noise to follow. Hitler's men were still causing terrible grief with these latest weapons. they were to continue until almost the end.

24 · To Buckingham Palace

Despite the horror of the V-weapons, the expected massive retaliation by the German bombers did not take place. Ken was on edge, after such a pressure period making sure that the men were ready to combat it. The away-from-the-action anti-climax was dreadful. He listened to the wireless news, read the newspapers avidly, wishing he was over in France.

But there were many others, locally and across the whole country, feeling much more that strange 'lost' feeling when let off danger. Men who had been selected for the overseas contingent, men standing ready to go – men soon to realise that the call was not coming.

Harold was also in a dilemma. His real 18th birthday was approaching and, when, he tried to realise his ambition and volunteer for the Royal Navy, the recruiting officer said 'No'. Clearly the fortunes of war had changed. He must wait to be called up, was the message. There was still work to be done, being ready for the 'Doodle Bugs'.

People watched as these new weapons of destruction chugged across the sky, with bated breath when the silence came as its engine stopped. These bombs, which they were literally, came crashing down to cause haphazard devastation – and yet more civilian victims. They cheered when a Spitfire or Typhoon came into view and, deliberately and calculating, touched wings to tilt the V.1s off balance and send another crashing down somewhere out of harm's way.

The day came for Harold's Call-up medical and interview. 'Interrogation,' he told Roger afterwards. But that was not surprising for he was determined to join the Royal Navy, and he fought and fought a robust verbal battle as the interviewers tried to dissuade him. At the end, just two from the whole town were still in the running. The other was accepted for the Royal Marines, and Harold for the Royal Navy, as a writer. His work as a journalist, and leadership, as the senior messenger of 15 Fire Force, had helped immensely.

To the fire service he returned, to admit his age and say he was leaving. Poetically, he learnt that letters were soon to be sent to all part-time NFS giving stand-down arrangements. 'Keep your equipment, report for duty at the main station if there was enemy action.' Clearly the 'war-time' stations were to close as quickly as they had opened. The Home Guard and Fire Guards had already stood down, the black-out was over.

It did not matter to Harold, now he found himself swept up in a new round of frenzied training. At least his varied young life, Scouts, Home Guard, and Fire Service, stood him in good stead in the Royal Navy. He could handle boats, tie knots, knew how to drill – and how to keep out of trouble – and, at last, fire that Lewis gun!

The shrill call of the bosun's pipe, followed by 'Stand Easy', gave him the chance to read the letter from Roger Smith. VE Day had been a work day in the Navy and, apparently, the fire service. But, the letter recounted how, two of the girls, Enid and Esther, real Londoners, had lived their ambition, and to hell with all the officers and discipline!

'I have always said that when peace is declared, I will have a party and go to Buckingham Palace.' Enid was talking to her sister, Esther. Both had just finished a tedious audit and were ready to escape from officialdom. 'Let's go,' she replied. 'There is to be an official proclamation from Buckingham Palace, and that's where I intend to be,' declared Enid.

'It's double pay, you will be in real trouble and you won't get paid,' said the other firewomen when told.

'I don't care about that, I have done my war work, that's the end of it.' Enid's mind was made up.

'The two sisters got up early, full of excitement, gathered together what patriotically coloured clothes they could find, put red, white and blue on their knickers, and went off on the train,' wrote Roger.

They took a boiled egg and bread and butter, there wasn't a lot of choice – they were lucky to have two eggs – for food. Paddington station, the excitement and the crowds increased. Their bus didn't travel far, it was stopped by the people streaming to Buckingham Palace. All traffic stopped.

By the time Enid and Esther reached Regents Street they were hungry, and ready to sit down. There were no seats, so they just sat down in the street and ate their boiled eggs. Nobody cared, it was that sort of special day.

So, complete with their red, white and blue knickers, they walked all the way to Buckingham Palace. 'I'm going to dance up Piccadilly,' declared Enid, more than ever excited by the mood of the capital. Outside the royal palace they were swallowed into the throng. Music was playing from speakers, everyone was chattering to everyone – with that same freedom they had learnt when being bombed, and those living in shelters, had found over the last five years. A slight movement at a palace window was enough to send messages through the gathering.

Then came the King and Queen, and others of the royal family. Cheers, complete ecstasy. Still the sisters stayed, caught up and spell-bound. 'Come on down, it's dinner time and we want some,' shouted Enid at the palace. Looking at each other they realised it was getting late: they had to catch the midnight train, there was no other until the next morning! Gradually, almost desperately they worked their way out of the crowd.

Eventually Enid and Esther reached Whitehall. Coming towards them was a stream of ATS and WAAFS, and others, all across the road and heading for Buckingham Palace. 'Girls, you're going the wrong way,' they all seemed to shout. 'No, we have to catch a train,' cried Enid. 'You're coming with us,' and both were swept up into a laughing, happy band of fellow types.

171

Off they went, back the way they had come, both waving their skirts to show the red, white and blue! It was a night, people across England will never forget.

'Next morning when they got back to Prospect Park mansion, there was a hell of a row going on,' wrote Roger. All Enid would say was, 'I'm not a bit interested. I enjoyed myself.' And they both got their double pay – 'For having the guts to go,' whispered their officer.

Back at the mansion, the other staff had been having fun as well. In the garden they found some wicker baskets of red wine. 'It must have been donkeys years old,' continued the letter. They strained it through blotting paper and drank it. 'Everybody must have been absolutely crazy with the excitement. One despatch rider was dancing on top of the desks in his pants.' The girls were having their own back, no more Gestapo, and had debagged him!'

*   *   *

Proudest moment for Gordon Castle was marching as one of a small band of firemen to take part in the Thanksgiving Service at St Paul's Cathedral on May 13th, 1945. He was selected to represent the whole of No 6 Region. A proud and deserved honour.

Thousands of people were lining the route through the capital's streets, as they marched from Cannon Street Fire Station. They were joining King George VI, and the Queen, and Princess Elizabeth. Also Winston Churchill. There were Generals Eisenhower, Montgomery, and de Gaulle; European ambassadors and foreign royalty.

'I believe we got a bigger cheer than anyone else as we marched. Londoners haven't forgotten. It is something I shall never forget,' he told his admiring fellow firemen, when he returned to Reading. 'All the Services were there, Navy, Army, Air Force, and the United States Army.'

'How different from those traumatic nights, not so long before!' said Ken as he shook his hand. 'Now its all over. The action stations have disappeared as fast as they were set up. Soon it will all be forgotten.'

*   *   *

Harold was sailing into Malta: the devastation was beyond anything in his experience. All along and around the quays everything was reduced to heaps of rubble. Out of this came dockyard workers, waving wildly at the ship – memories were still sufficiently vivid to welcome any ship which could make it to the George Cross island.

VJ Day – Victory over Japan – had been marked, when Harold received another letter from Roger. This was full of the celebrations. Why not? This was really the end of the danger and despair the firemen and women, alike, had faced bravely.

Jane had driven her car, with three other firewomen, out into Berkshire, to the Boot Inn at Blewbury, on the downs. It was a night to use petrol coupons. A new world was starting.

'You could never guess how excited people were,' wrote Roger. 'Although, I suppose you would really, you know what they have been through.' There were a lot of soldiers at the pub and, before they knew what was happening, the girls were being tossed from soldier to soldier.

'In a few years time people will never dream of doing things like that but, on that night it was fun. Nobody was hurt and no advantage was taken.'

When the girls were going home, they reached Pangbourne. The Thames-side village's square was just one solid mass of people. 'Oh God, how are we going to get through here,' thought Jane. The other three got out, leaving Jane. She reached the middle of the crowd. Suddenly people got hold of the car and started lifting it up and down! Then, they all laughed and let her go on.

'A fine lot of pals you are, leaving me ...' said Jane. 'We were frightened. We imagined they were going over the top,' was their reply. For Jane, who had driven fire vehicles all over the place, it was the final excitement before they all stood down.

*   *   *

'Britain shall not burn.' These watchwords of the Home Secretary were recalled when the National Fire Service's senior officers paid tribute. The Chief Regional Fire Officer, H M Smith, and the three Fire Force Commanders, including D M Taylor, wrote 'expressing our sincere appreciation to all part-time members of the NFS in the Southern Region, for the loyal support during these arduous and trying years of war.'

Their message went on, 'We have known only too well how difficult it must have been for you to meet the many demands made upon you, particularly in view of the long hours you have spent in your normal employment in office, factory and on the land.

'Now that the country is free from the danger of enemy air attack, you can lay down your equipment with the knowledge that you have completed a most difficult and dangerous task, in the performance of which you have brought great credit to the Service and have earned the gratitude of the Nation.'

*   *   *

Gibraltar was the next work place for Harold, sent to join the staff of the Admiral commanding the Mediterranean Approaches. It was there, just before Christmas, that he received a sad letter from Roger. It was to say that Leading Fireman 'Sibby' Beeson, who had led the messengers with the field telephone van, had been killed.

'He served all through the war without getting hurt. Now, when everything is peaceful ...' Harold could see in his mind, the fireman who had been so kind to him, trying to pen his thoughts. 'He was thrown from a fire appliance at Walling-ford. It goes to show that firemen always risk more than people realise.'

173